HIPPIES IN THE CITY

HIPPIES IN THE CITY

a guide to natural urban living

BY RITA BALSHAW

hippies IN THE CITY

First published in 2012
An imprint of Rita Balshaw

Hippies in the City™ has been trademarked 1464087
www.hippiesinthecity.com

National Library of Australia Cataloguing-in-Publication entry
Author: Balshaw, Rita
Title: Hippies in the City / Rita Balshaw
IBSN: 9780646577074 (PBK.)
Subjects: Well being. Organic living. Health.
Dewey Number: 613

Cover design: Michelle Terry
Internal design: Gloria Tsang / Green Olive Press
Illustrations: Michelle Terry
Printed using sustainable methods of printing.

WAMBOOL PRINTING SOLUTIONS

pH NEUTRAL
ARCHIVAL

ECF ELEMENTAL
CHLORINE FREE

EMS ENVIRONMENTAL
MANAGEMENT SYSTEMS

This book is dedicated
to everyone committed
to helping others...
Thank you to all the
people in the world who
contribute by giving
something back...

ACKNOWLEDGEMENTS

I wish to thank all those who have helped me, inspired me and believed in me. Firstly I would like to express my appreciation to the founders of Perfect Potion, Salvatore Battaglia and Carolyn Stubbin who provided the opportunity and encouragement to explore the wonderful world of natural therapies. Further thanks to Ren Chew, Arash Rostami, Michelle Terry, Caroline Webber and Alana Leuzzi for their creative and technical support. A special thanks goes to my wonderful friends and family, who fill my heart with joy and are the driving force behind my existence.

ABOUT THE AUTHOR

"To my Great Loves... Good Food, Good Sounds and Good Smells."

I am committed to helping others – devoted to a core philosophy of food as medicine. My intense passion for natural therapies combined with the drive to educate others was all the inspiration needed to put together *Hippies in the City*. With all my heart I believe that the food we eat affects our physical body, emotional intelligence and spiritual growth.

After completing studies in nutrition, business studies, holistic counselling and gaining almost six years' experience working for Perfect Potion, one of Australia's leading aromatherapy companies, I began collating my knowledge of everything involving food, aromatherapy, clean living, cooking and basically anything I had read, studied and experienced over the last 28 years. In 2010 I was a Top 10 finalist in the Australian Miss Earth competition, and participated as an ambassador representing young women in Australia who contribute to solving environmental issues.

The constant desire to want to assist people change their lives – psychologically and nutritionally – was the true inspiration behind this book. Growing up, my days were filled with cooking amazing food for friends and family. As I reflect on my life as a young woman, the images that come to mind are of me in the kitchen, shopping at second-hand and vintage stores, planting trees, reading health magazines, making potions and lotions and basically doing anything that involved a holistic way of life. Some of us are born into this way of life; others aspire to live this way. Finding myself sitting on trains, buses and planes sharing stories of cooking, nutrition and aromatherapy advice, I thought it was about time I shared these things with the world.

Most of us have been given something beautiful in this life... the freedom of investigation. Everything in this book comes from me. My claims are solely based on my own personal study and experience. I have not spent any time in a laboratory, nor do I hold a degree in medical science. I have, however, spent hours in the kitchen, and years writing, reading and travelling, exploring the wonderful art of food and natural therapies. Investigate anything you read, trust your intuition and take bits and pieces of knowledge from all sources, rolling with whatever feels right for your body and soul.

Thank you for reading. I pray that everyone who reads this book experiences inner peace and accomplishes the real meaning of life and I truly hope you feel inspired, enlightened and appreciative of your bodies.

Rita Balshaw

CONTENTS

The Organic Priority
Certifications
Nutritionally Holistic
A to Z
Activate Your Nuts
Be GMO-free
Cooking With Kindness
Why Detox?
Discover the Significance of Eating
Does Age Really Matter?
Fifty – Fifty
Get Sexual
High Tea
How Does a Hippy Fight a Cold?
Karma Man
Macrobiotic
Milk Me
Nature's Gatorade
Not Tonight Honey
Povo
Preggers
Ritual
Seasonal Living
Secret Garden
Skinny Bitch
Sleep Easy
So What's the Story With Aromatherapy Food?
Something to Digest
Spirulina – the Super Food
Sweet Enough
Thank Krishna for the Hare Food
The Cave Man Diet
The Goat v the Cow
The Inconvenient Truth

INTRODUCTION

"A guide to living in harmony with yourself and the natural world."

Hippies in the City is a charming book you can take anywhere to inspire you to live a more nourishing and abundant existence through food, natural therapies and a holistic approach to life. It aims to deepen your relationship with, and respect for, the natural world, by introducing you to exciting food and health facts and provides helpful advice on your needs. Also included are easy-to-prepare wholesome recipes using ingredients that quickly transform your health and wellbeing.

Written in a fun and personal way, *Hippies in the City* invites you into a holistic world highlighting all the wonderful things you can create using only 100 per cent natural and unprocessed ingredients. *Hippies in the City* is a collection of recipes for food and skincare, food philosophies, self-help (aka hippy advice), daily quotes, sustainable living tips and includes a holistic directory.

Holistic methods are explored, focusing on how to live in a fast-paced environment and stay wholesomely nourished by learning how to live simply, eat healthily and enhance your life naturally. Nature truly does provide for us. Become a hippy in the city... learn where to go, what to eat, how to cook.

Disclaimer note:
These food and lifestyle suggestions are based on my own research conclusions and should not be taken as medical advice. The content of this book is the sole expression and opinion of the author.

HIPPY RULES & REGULATIONS

CERTIFIED ORGANIC
It is preferable that all recipes and remedies in this book are made with 100 per cent certified organic food, essential oils and raw materials. However, if you can't afford organic produce, please don't miss out, just create them anyway using regular ingredients.

PLAY IT FORWARD
Buy someone a copy of this book. In doing so you are giving the gift of health to another. The ideas and information may just change someone's life, directing them on the path to a more abundant existence. When *Hippies in the City* was first published, I sent a copy to a random address in each state of Australia. What goes around always comes around.

TAKE ME WITH YOU
Take me to work, to the park, to a sleepover at a friend's house or to a café as a lunch date. This book likes to go on adventures. *Hippies in the City* is a user's guide covering the topics that will help you to lead a more natural life and sustainable existence. Use and refer to the book as much as you possibly can.

NOTES

CHAPTER ONE

HIPPY INFORMATION

"Knowledge is one of the greatest gifts we can give to one another. The exchange of information is indeed a human obligation. Learning about your health and mastering your wellbeing will serve you greatly. Always do your research, listen to your intuition and carefully observe your body when it comes to health advice."

THE ORGANIC PRIORITY

"Learn from yesterday, live for today, and dream about the possibilities of tomorrow."

Okay, so if you have the cash, buy organic food and skincare. It's just better; better for the environment, better for your health and it certainly tastes and feels better. Organic, pesticide free, wildcrafted and biodynamic food contains no harmful preservatives or additives and is GMO-free. Organic food has a higher nutritional value, making you feel healthy and energised.

Non-organic grains, fruits and vegetables are sprayed with pesticides. These are a very harmful blend of chemicals that are toxic. It is excellent news that some non-organic foods are not as affected by pesticides, and are therefore not as harmful. It is wise to support sustainable farming methods and whenever possible buy non-sprayed and organic produce. If organic vegetables are not accessible it is important that you thoroughly wash non-organic produce before eating it. Washing fruit and vegetables in citrus seed extract, green clay or baking soda are all effective methods for removing excess chemical residue.

CERTIFICATIONS

"Live simply so others can continue to live."

A stamp of organic certification ensures that the products and services you support are legitimate. Organically certified companies pay a lot of money and work very hard to sustain their stamp of certification, allowing consumers to feel safe and enjoy a superior product.

AUSTRALIAN CERTIFIED ORGANIC (ACO) – Organic certification is obtained when an organic certifying group audits a business and its methods to ensure that it complies with national and international standards for organic farming and processing. The organic standards place great emphasis on creating and maintaining healthy soil, nutritious crops and animal welfare practices. The ACO logo is found on food and skincare products.
WWW.AUSTRALIANORGANIC.COM.AU

THE NATIONAL ASSOCIATION FOR SUSTAINABLE AGRICULTURE, AUSTRALIA (NASAA) – This association is dedicated to developing and maintaining organic standards. It assists operators to attain organic certification, and conducts ongoing compliance supervision and inspection of all certified operations. The logo can be found on grocery products, meat, wine and cheese.
WWW.NASAA.COM.AU

ORGANIC GROWERS OF AUSTRALIA (OGA) – This program is for small producers, with a gross annual income of less than $75,000. The process is simpler and less expensive than other organic programs, making it accessible and user-friendly for the smaller producer to become certified organic. It is primarily found on the foodstuffs sold at farmers markets.
WWW.ORGANICGROWERS.ORG.AU

FAIR TRADE – Fair trade addresses the injustices of conventional trade. It ensures that disadvantaged farmers and workers in developing countries get a fair deal through the use of the International Fair Trade Certification Mark. This certification stamp can be found on tea, coffee, chocolate products and skincare.
WWW.FTA.ORG.AU

CHOOSE CRUELTY FREE (CCF) – This is an independent non-profit organisation, which actively promotes a cruelty-free lifestyle. CCF encourages manufacturers and service providers to make people aware of their power, as consumers, to change attitudes about testing products on animals. CCF lists organisations that do not test on animals. The CCF logo is printed on skincare and make-up products.
WWW.CHOOSECRUELTYFREE.ORG.AU

BDIH CERTIFIED NATURAL COSMETICS – BDIH is the Association of German Industries and Trading Firms for pharmaceuticals, health care products, food supplements and personal hygiene products. Only products that meet the very strict standards of the BDIH guidelines are able to display the BDIH Certified Natural Cosmetics symbol, which can be found on food, skincare and make-up products.
WWW.KONTROLLIERTE-NATURKOSMETIK.DE

NUTRITIONALLY HOLISTIC

"Happiness is a choice. Today I choose to be happy, because it is good for my health. Every day we have a choice, to build our health, or produce illness."

Holistic nutrition is all about having a natural diet and lifestyle that your body understands. We need a certain balance of nutrients to reach maximum energy levels and improve our overall physical and emotional health.

The purpose of eating food is to nourish your body by supplying it with vitamins, minerals, proteins, amino acids, antioxidants and essential fatty acids. When a person's diet is poor, they are deprived. Their immunity is weak; their organs are depressed; they are dull and listless, and conditions are optimal for bacteria and cancer cells to grow.

Diet and nutrition have a profound impact on mental and physical health. I believe your kitchen is your pharmacy, your personal laboratory of experimentation. I want you, my readers to learn how to cook, and enjoy wholesome natural food in your home every day. I find it so empowering that a cure to pretty much all health problems can be found in my garden and kitchen. Food is truly a universal medicine.

Humans should be aware, present, sharp, energetic, clear minded, happy and relaxed. Our skin should be clear and reasonably odourless; our bodies flexible; our eyes bright; our teeth and gums healthy; our nails and hair should grow long and strong. We should not be overweight. If you are slow, angry, depressed, confused, have allergies, are overweight, have irregular periods, feel stiff, suffer from skin conditions, get headaches, are diseased, sleep poorly, feel lethargic or fatigued and have a poor sex drive maybe you should look at your diet and make changes towards a more holistic lifestyle. By doing so the rewards of a healthy mind and body are endless.

HOLISTIC NUTRITION RULES

- Eat wholefoods in their natural state
- All food should be organic and locally sourced
- Buy unpackaged and fresh produce
- Only purchase organic non-homogenised and unpasteurised dairy products
- No junk or processed food
- No preservatives, food acids, additives or artificial ingredients
- No refined or artificial sugar
- No use of microwaves
- No genetically modified (GM) food
- Drink adequate amounts of pure water
- Attend to nutritional deficiencies

A TO Z

"With proper diet and lifestyle there is no need for medicine. With in proper diet and lifestyle there is no use for medicine"

A

A is for apples. Some of the most disease-fighting components are found in the apple. Apples are found to improve lung health, making them great for those with asthma. They are also an excellent weight control food as they are high in insoluble fibre and pectin, leaving you feeling satisfied. Munch on an organic apple every day as a sweet snack or after dinner to curb cravings.

B

B is for buckwheat, the best known source of high biological value proteins in the plant kingdom. It's a great bread and pasta alternative for those who struggle with wheat allergies and gluten intolerance. Buckwheat is healthy, hearty and delicious. It is high in insoluble fibre and has plenty of protein and B vitamins. It is also rich in phosphorus, potassium, magnesium, iron, and calcium.

C

Cherries contain plenty of beta-carotene, the ultimate cancer fighter. Cherries are also a nightcap fruit as they contain melatonin, the hormone that regulates sleep. They are high in vitamin C, taste sensationally sweet, and in Australia remind us of the summer holidays! A dark chocolate and cherry combination is the bomb!

D

D is for keeping a personal diary. Writing down your thoughts daily is powerful because it makes you think deeply about the things that are important to you. By keeping a log of your progress, pain, pleasures and pursuits you will be able to sort out frustrated thoughts and calm your outlook on life. When you reflect on your diary it will encourage you and keep you accountable as you work to meet goals.

E

E is for the environment that we owe a big hug to! We can make up for past damage by consciously starting to live a more sustainable lifestyle. Sustainable living is all about making choices that will preserve the planet for generations to come. It is never too late to do your bit for the planet and even the smallest of things can make a huge difference to our environment.

F

Is for the ever so fabulous fig. Dried or fresh, either way they are absolutely amazing. Since figs are among the most highly alkaline foods they are wonderful for supporting the pH balance of your body. Figs have a high fibre content, so they are often recommended to nourish and tone the intestines.

G

The grapefruit is not just the largest citrus fruit around, it is also a fruit that holds a huge amount of vitamin C, making these big yellow balls of goodness astounding for wound healing, heart health, relieving cold symptoms and improving the health of the skin. Bursting with bitter sweetness, add grapefruit to salads or juice with ginger, apple, pineapple and mint to cleanse and fire up the metabolism.

H

Herbs man! Plants have been used for medicinal purposes for thousands of years. Ancient Chinese, Indian and Egyptian writings describe medicinal uses for plants. Africans and Native Americans used herbs in their healing rituals. Other cultures developed natural medical systems, such as Ayurveda and Traditional Chinese Medicine in which herbal therapies are still widely used.

I

Iquitos is the largest city in the rainforest of Peru. Located on the Amazon River, it is a place for seekers, rather than sightseers. Many visit Iquitos for shamanic ceremonies and spiritual healing. Shamanism is used for psychic, emotional, and spiritual healing. It is also a path for exploration and discovery, of non-material worlds and states of mind.

J

J will be dedicated to Sir Jamie Oliver because his attitude to food and cooking is indescribably inspirational. Jamie is a man who truly loves, respects and lives for cooking. His understanding of food is absolutely captivating and his dedication to good eating is honourable.

K

The beautifully bitter kale is an excellent source of immunity-pumping nutrients. It is a rather awesome supplier of vitamins B1, B2, and E, dietary fibre, iron, copper and calcium. Place it on a baking tray, sprinkle with a little sea salt and turmeric powder and cook for 15 minutes to make your own crunchy kale chips.

L

Linseed, also known as flaxseed, is now recognised as one of today's super foods. It is a nutritional powerhouse of essential fatty acids which strengthen the immune system and cleanse the blood. Flaxseeds and their oil are highly anti-inflammatory and are a good source of fibre, protein, B vitamins, magnesium, potassium and zinc.

M

M is for the magical maca powder. Maca is used to balance the endocrine system, which influences almost every cell, organ, and function in the human body. The endocrine system is instrumental in regulating mood, growth and development, tissue function, metabolism, sexual function and reproductive health.

N

Nori is definitely the star in the world of seaweeds and anyone who knows their sushi knows that seaweed is full of vitamin C, vitamin A, potassium, magnesium and riboflavin (B2). Nori is also rich in iodine, iron and protein. Use shredded nori in salads and Asian style stir-fries.

O

O is for the Okinawa people of Japan! The Japanese live longer than anyone else in the world. They follow a principle of only eating until you are 80 per cent full, following a simple diet of organic rice, green vegetables, green tea, seaweed and fish. These people employ the practice of listening to the body's own intelligence.

P

Probiotics are a must for better gut health. They are especially essential for people who have just completed a course of antibiotics; have been travelling overseas; undergo regular colonic therapy or suffer from digestive and stomach issues such as IBS, coeliac disease, allergies, Crohn's disease, gas and bloating.

Q

Q is for our qi, pronounced 'chee'. In Chinese culture, qi is commonly referred to as life energy, life force or energy flow. The fundamental purpose of correcting the energy of the body in Traditional Chinese Medicine is that balanced and free-flowing qi results in health, where as stagnant or imbalanced qi leads to disease.

R

From Italy to India to Indonesia, rice has been feeding the world for thousands of years. Most Asian countries depend on it as a staple food. Whether brown, red or white, all rice are of the same grain. Rice is a good source of vitamins and minerals. Brown rice provides protein, which contains the essential amino acids. All rice is high in complex carbohydrates and low in fat.

S

S is for the seaweeds like kombu, wakame, and nori harvested from the wondrous ocean and highly nutritious. Seaweeds are extraordinarily rich in minerals and trace elements, including iron, potassium, calcium, folate and iodine, as well as vitamins A, C and B-complex. Add seaweeds to salads and soups and enjoy their immense nutritional benefits.

T

Thiamine, also called vitamin B1, is a water-soluble B-complex vitamin. Essential for all the stress heads out there, B vitamins greatly assist to manage stress within the body. Thiamine is needed for normal growth and development. It also helps to sustain proper functioning of the heart and nervous system.

U

U is for unrefined sugar. Unlike refined sugar, natural unrefined sugars contain trace minerals, and it's these minerals that make palm sugar, rapadura cane sugar, honey and agave preferable to use. There are many alternatives to refined sugar that are neither toxic nor damaging to the body, which white refined sugar is.

V

V is for the vibration of your food. The more fresh and nutrient rich the foods you eat are, the higher the energetic vibration. Raw super foods have a very high vibration and cleanse and enliven every living system in the body. They wake up the body's innate intelligence for health; the cells detoxify and start functioning optimally, providing more energy, harmony and mental clarity to illuminate and sustain you.

W

W is for wholefoods. Wholefood is food in its natural state. The opposite of wholefood is processed food that has been pulled apart, mostly for increased shelf life, resulting in diminished nutritional content. A pear, a banana, a carrot, a piece of meat, a grain of brown rice, a lentil - these are wholefoods. Your body understands food in its whole form. When eaten, optimum health is achieved.

X

Xanthium gum is a natural plant-derived thickening agent that can be used in cooking. It is also good for making your own gel based skincare products because it stabilises and binds.

Y

Choose yoghurt that is made from kefir and coconut cream because it is a delicious, cultured, enzyme-rich food, filled with friendly micro-organisms that help balance your own inner ecosystem. Kefir and coconut yoghurt is far more nutritious and therapeutic than cow's milk yoghurt because it supplies complete protein, essential minerals, and precious B vitamins.

Z

Mum, I'm not eating those bikinis! The funky zucchini is abundant in dietary fibre, which greatly helps lower cholesterol. Zucchinis will always be an old school favourite because they contain numerous health benefits, and have a delightful texture and taste used in dishes such as casseroles, stews and even muffins and cakes. Coat thin slices of zucchini with a whisked egg, dust in rice flour, and fry in rice bran oil until golden. Then sprinkle with sea salt for a scrumptious, savoury treat.

ACTIVATE YOUR NUTS!

"Imagination is everything. It is the preview of life's coming even ᵕ. A true sign of intelligence is not knowledge alone, but imagination."

Activated nuts are easy to digest and more nutritious than those that are raw or roasted. By activating or soaking and sprouting nuts, an enzyme inhibitor is released, allowing nutrients to be effectively absorbed by the body. Usually when we eat nuts and seeds they are inactive, hibernating in their little hard skins, keeping all their goodness to themselves. The humble nut and seeds are not naturally this selfish; they just need a little help in releasing all they have to offer you nutritionally.

The science behind this theory is logical; by soaking raw nuts and seeds in purified water it stimulates the process of germination and increases their nutritional value. Activated nuts and seeds taste so much better, expressing lots more flavour and crunch.

So, you're probably thinking 'how the heck do I activate my nuts?' Well, it's quite simple really. Soak your preferred nuts for 24 hours in filtered water, then rinse and dehydrate them at 40°C for 24 hours. If you don't have a dehydrator, place your soaked nuts on an oven tray and roast them in a warm oven at a low temperature for two hours. Check the nuts every half an hour. You will know they are ready when they're crunchy and slightly roasted.

If you like savoury nuts, lightly sprinkle them with sea salt, cayenne pepper and turmeric before roasting. If you like your nuts a little sweeter, add a sprinkle of sea salt, palm sugar and maple syrup before roasting.

BE GMO-FREE

"There is no need to tamper with perfection; it's the imperfections that often make something perfect."

GMO means genetically modified organism, an organism created by scientists when they genetically modify or engineer food and plants. There are environmental risks associated with genetically modified (GM) foods, and there is a growing concern that introducing foreign genes into food and plants may have a negative impact on our health. Crops that are at high risk of being genetically engineered are soy, rice, alfalfa, canola, corn, cotton, flaxseed, papaya, squash and zucchini. Animal derivatives like milk, meat, eggs, and honey are also considered high risk, because of the potential GMO pollution in the food the animals eat.

AVOID NON-GMO FOODS BY;

- Eating organically - Buying organic foods offers assurance against the risks of consuming GM substances because they are prohibited in organic production.

- Buying locally grown foods - There is nothing better than locally produced meat, fresh fruits and vegetables. Buying locally supports local farmers and keeps food dollars in the community. It also means you know more about the food you and your family are consuming.

- Growing your own - Gardening is indeed a great hobby. It nourishes the body, mind, and soil! Growing and producing your own anything is the ultimate way to live. Learn how to live sustainably to enrich your life and save you some coins, too.

For more information visit WWW.NONGMOPROJECT.ORG

COOKING WITH KINDNESS

"Love and kindness are never wasted, they always make a difference."

Meat is a food for celebration, a ceremonial commodity that deserves great appreciation and respect. Show your gratitude for the animal that has died for you, by giving thanks for all the abundance that the meat has to offer your body – iron, iodine and vitamin B12. These are essential vitamins and minerals that promote the formation of red and white blood cells and improve muscle function.

From a nutritional and food safety point of view, eating organic or free-range meat is better for our health. An organic meat expert would not eat non-organic meat because conventionally raised and factory farmed animals are treated with hormones and antibiotics, and feed from chemically saturated grains. Organically raised animals are grass fed so their meat is more nutritious and tastes a billion times better than non-organic meat. If you limit meat intake and reduce portion size, you will find that organic meat becomes affordable.

Australians eat way too much meat and poultry and need to limit their intake. Humans do not require excessive amounts of meat to obtain their nutritional requirements. In a world that is running out of oil and water, farming is incredibly taxing on the environment. Opt for more of a vegetarian-style diet because it is better for our health and our planet.

For more information visit WWW.MEATFREEMONDAYS.COM

WHY DETOX?

"When the body is pure, the mind is pure; when the mind is pure, the spirit is pure."

In Traditional Chinese Medicine an ailing liver is thought to be the cause of all allergies. It is believed that if the liver is sluggish it cannot clear toxins effectively from the body, making the immune system weak. This results in allergic symptoms such as eczema and psoriasis. The best way to improve a sluggish liver is to reduce your intake of foods that congest and irritate the lymphatic system – refined carbohydrates, sugar, dairy, coffee, alcohol, cigarettes and drugs.

Detoxification involves the deactivation of toxins and their removal from the body. When toxin levels are too high for effective detoxification, the body protects itself by storing toxins in fat. During a detox, toxins are liberated from storage into the bloodstream. It is normal to feel nauseous or headachy during a detox. Once the toxins are transformed by the liver and excreted, a feeling of lightness and clarity replaces a stagnant heaviness. Cleansing clears old rubbish from the body, leaving you with more energy, bright eyes, clear skin and a great sense of wellbeing.

Our world is becoming increasingly toxic. Daily, we are confronted by synthetic chemicals, personal care and cleaning products, air pollutants, contaminants in our washing and drinking water, bleach in our tea bags, pesticide residues and artificial additives in our foods. Most illnesses result from an accumulation of toxic waste in the body and regular internal cleansing and supportive detoxification programs are paramount to ongoing health and disease prevention.

How to Detox

Naturopathic philosophy maintains that a vital force works within our bodies to continually move us towards balance and health. A naturopathic detox is a program that involves three basic, equally important parts: minimising toxin intake, promoting toxin elimination and minimising harm caused by toxins.

- We must alkalise our bodies. The easiest way to do this is through supplementation with green foods and drinks that contain liquid chlorophyll.

- There are numerous herbs and nutritional supplements to optimise liver function, including the amino acids arginine and methionine, and herbs such as turmeric, globe artichoke, dandelion root and milk thistle.

- Drinking purified water supports detoxification and is great for kidney health. Cleansing herbal teas such as nettle and red clover are also detoxifying.

DISCOVER THE SIGNIFICANCE OF EATING

"Life can be as pleasurable or as painful as we allow it to be."

Eating is about nourishing the body, providing it with fuel to create energy so that it can work and protect it against disease. Often we eat for other reasons than to satisfy hunger and gain sustenance. It is important to keep in mind that gluttony does not serve you physically or emotionally. Meal times are times for nourishment. Eat your food slowly and mindfully in a quiet, comfortable space paying attention to the tastes, textures and smells of your meal. Try not to become too rigid about eating habits, as circumstances sometimes require us to be flexible. Remember that enjoyment and relaxation are as important as what you eat during meals.

Slow down and be grateful for your food. There is a direct relationship between what you eat, who you are and who you will become. Food is certainly an enjoyable sensory delight, however, we need to understand that eating is not just about taste, it's primarily about nourishment. What we put in our mouth directly affects our physical and emotional wellbeing. The best approach is to mindfully eat wholefoods that contribute to our health and wellbeing.

DOES AGE REALLY MATTER?

"I don't judge others, nor do I judge myself. We are all doing our very best in this wonderful life. I am blessed just to be. I am grateful for what life has given me."

When it comes to preventing premature ageing, you really need to know who the culprits are - refined and artificial sugars, processed meat, refined salt, refined carbohydrates, soft drinks, alcohol, cigarettes, drugs, excessive sun exposure, stress, guilt, worry, pollution, dehydration, preservatives and artificial foods. All anti-ageing nutrition must include significant amounts of vitamins, minerals and essential fatty acids. There is a group of substances known as antioxidants that play an important role in keeping you young and looking sensational, as they neutralize what scientists call free radicals. Free radicals set off a chain reaction in our bodies that kills cells, destroys cell membranes and mutates DNA. It doesn't matter whether you are in your twenties or forties, the sooner you become conscious about protecting your body against premature ageing the better you will look and feel. The easiest and cheapest way to ingest these antioxidants is through food – eat aesthetically nourishing food high in antioxidants that strengthen your internal organs and skin, to slow down the ageing process.

H2O IS THE GO

Every cell in your body requires water. The best thing you can do for your complexion and overall health is to drink alot of it. Drinking plenty of pure and clean water keeps your skin hydrated, flushes toxins from the tissues of the body, supports organ function and reduces the appearance of fine lines and wrinkles. Water should be your primary drink.

BANGING BERRIES

Cranberries, raspberries, blackberries, mulberries, goji berries and blueberries are packed full of antioxidants and other nutrients your body needs to make repairs and prevent free radical damage. Also, berries taste really, really good. They are a great source of vitamin A and C as well as phytochemicals that help to strengthen cells and collagen production, and boost immunity. Include berries in your diet for a healthy glow.

GREENERY

It can be pretty boring to talk about the importance of eating more vegetables, but we all really need to do it! If everyone ate five or more servings of fruits and vegetables each day, we'd see a huge decrease in heart disease, cancer, high blood pressure and other diseases. Make an effort to eat more veggies this week,. Ideally we should eat 10 servings a day. Focus on leafy or deeply coloured vegetables like kale, kelp, spinach, rocket and seaweeds for the most anti-ageing benefits.

Avocados the creamy fruit

Avocados top the anti-ageing foods list because they are so delicious, and full of minerals and healthy fats that lower cholesterol and make the skin supple. Avocados are loaded with vitamin E, the vitamin that specialises in skin healing and repair.

Walnuts, more than a nut

Like salmon and linseeds, walnuts are a great source of omega-3 essential fatty acids, one of the finest and immensely beneficial dietary fatty acids known on this planet. Eat a handful or two a day for all your omega-3 needs. Eating foods that contain significant amounts of omega-3 makes your skin noticeably smooth and supple.

The greenest of tea

Green tea has been the long life supplement in Asia for thousands of years. Drinking green tea daily is highly beneficial because it contains high concentrations of antioxidants and phytochemicals your body needs to stay healthy. It provides a mild energy boost due to its natural low caffeine content.

Red, red wine

Woo hoo, red wine is good for you! It contains a substance called resveratrol that helps your body fight off age-related illnesses. At the end of the week have a glass or two of organic red wine to relax and unwind. Here in hippy land we choose an organically certified wine wherever possible.

Mr Bean

Beans are a great source of protein and antioxidants offering your body an array of nutrients to restore the health of your skin. Beans truly are a wonder food, and switching to a more healthy vegetarian style diet will certainly help improve the skin tone and its elasticity.

See-Food

Prawns, mussels, fish... you name it, seafood is rich in zinc and omega-3 essential fatty acids sensational for skin, hair and nails. You will find the longest living cultures, with the clearest and most sparkling skin, are those with a high seafood diet.

Chocolate

Sugarless and organic dark chocolate is excellent for you, because cocoa is bursting with beneficial vitamins and minerals. It also possesses healthy fats and nutrients that your skin needs for optimal health and vitality. Read the label to ensure the chocolate doesn't contain refined sugar. Have a few squares every so often, to keep you glowing and cheerful.

Good oils

Try adding a capful of extra virgin, evening primrose, flaxseed or macadamia oil to your food. You can cook with these oils, but if you want the benefits of their full therapeutic properties enjoy them unheated. Although many plant oils are high in fat, these are nourishing fats that support the entire health of your body. If you are active and eat well you won't put on weight when you eat monounsaturated and polyunsaturated fats.

Mediterranean

The Mediterranean diet has been praised for decades as being one of the healthiest, and is adored all over the world. Although this way of eating can be somewhat challenging to the waistline, it sure keeps the skin young, smooth and extremely supple. Legumes, nuts, fruits, beans, vegetables, seafood, poultry, fish, whole grains, olives and olive oil, red wine and little red meat are the main foods included in the Mediterranean diet.

Superman foods

I have watched different super foods go in and out of fashion, become popular, fade out and become popular again. Goji berries, acai berries, spirulina, cocoa, wheatgrass, maca, millet, chia seeds, olive leaf extract, noni juice and many other super foods are abundant in antioxidants and may hold the secret key to prolonged existence.

Carrots

Carrots are an excellent source of vitamin A, an essential nutrient for healthy skin. Carrots contain high levels of antioxidants, which prevent free radical damage to skin cells. When skin cells are protected from harm and disintegration, your face will look younger and healthier for longer.

Additional anti-ageing secrets

Yoga and meditation keep the body and mind relaxed and free from stress (the major ageing perpetrator) ensuring on a cellular level your whole being is healthy and happy. Moisturising your body from head to toe every day, first with oil then with cream that contains organic vegetable and essential oils, ensures your skin stays smooth, supple and hydrated.

FIFTY – FIFTY

"The vitamins and minerals of raw foods, and the easy digestion of the cooked."

Often, the closer food is to its natural state, the better it is for you, suggesting foods that are cooked will lose and damage some of it's nutritional value. Not too long ago some smarty pants came up with the concept of the raw food diet, only eating food in its raw and natural state. Obviously the drive behind this much talked about trend is getting the most from your food by eating raw vegetables, fruits, sprouted grains, seeds, and nuts without diminishing any of the nutritional benefits caused by cooking. Raw foods are high in enzymes, vitamins and minerals. Cooking certain foods can harm the bioavailability of the protein and several heat sensitive vitamins. Some of the vitamins harmed by cooking are vitamin A, thiamine, folate, and vitamin C. Fresh and organic raw foods give you more energy and feel somewhat cleaner for the body and mind.

On the other hand, eating cooked food is also important. Warm food is easy to digest. There is no point in eating unless the food is being digested properly. I will never stop cooking. I never could! So, I have a solution – 50 percent raw food and 50 percent cooked food. Maybe in the summer months you could up it to 70 percent raw and 30 percent cooked, and in the cooler months enjoy more cooked meals; this way you get the best of both worlds. The 50 percent raw food and 50 percent cooked food is the perfect ratio for a healthy diet. What I like to do to implement this balance is create meals that are also 50-50 raw and cooked. For breakfast I will have a boiled egg and fresh fruit; for lunch, steamed brown rice and organic raw vegetables; for dinner, baked fish and a fresh salad.

GET SEXUAL

"I am ready to honour my body and embrace my sexuality."

An aphrodisiac is a substance that increases sexual desire, because feeling in the mood is one of those things that comes and goes. The flow of sexuality will differ from one individual to another, depending on life circumstance, physical and emotional health, spiritual beliefs and energetic blockages. It is important to use one's sexual energy in an uplifting way, in order to live happily and creatively.

DAMIANA HERBAL TEA AND TINCTURE – Damiana has an intense aphrodisiac effect, making you feel desirable and relaxed about sexual connection. It has long been used for improving sexual health and overcoming anxiety.

MACA POWDER – Sometimes called 'Peru's Viagra', Peruvian maca both increases libido and acts as an aphrodisiac. As a result, both fertility and sexual desire are improved after consuming this organic super food.

RAW COCOA - The Aztecs referred to cocoa as the nourishment of the gods. Raw cocoa is loaded with phenylethylamine, which is the hormone released during sex, making you feel a strong sense of excitement. Eating cocoa lifts your vibration, promoting feelings of connection and wellbeing.

OYSTERS – These are well known for their aphrodisiac properties. Their high zinc content increases libido and also helps produce sperm. Ooh la la let's order some oysters!

ORGANIC EPIMEDIUM (HORNY GOAT WEED) – Epimedium, also known as horny goat weed, is a herbal remedy that is used to improve sexual energy and stamina. It is always good to seek advice from a health professional before taking herbal supplements.

ORGANIC KOREAN GINSENG – Organic Korean Ginseng is capable of increasing sexual activity and sperm production, and is widely used to enhance overall physical and mental performance.

EXPLORE THE SACRAL CHAKRA – The sacral chakra is associated with your sexual and creative energy, which rotates around your pelvis, lower back and reproductive organs. When the sacral chakra energy is blocked you feel sexually disconnected, creatively blocked and sad.

AROMATHERAPY – Ylang ylang, jasmine, rose, sandalwood and patchouli essential oils are exceptional for enhancing happiness and sexual desires. Massage, burn or bathe in these essential oils whenever you feel in the mood or are trying to persuade another to get in the mood.

HIGH TEA

The tradition of tea drinking dates back to BC times; tea drinking still remains a universal practice."

Choose organic tea because it is produced using safe and sustainable agricultural practices. The best way to brew a good cuppa is to scoop one tablespoonful of herbs per cup into a pot or infuser. Before pouring in the boiling water, cover the herbs with a little cold water, so you don't shock them, and their medicinal properties remain strong. Herbal tea brewing time is generally five to ten minutes.

The tea ceremony, whether it is by yourself or with friends, is about unity, tradition and intention. Drinking herbal teas are a great way to keep the body hydrated and cleansed. There are countless varieties of herbal tea you can drink to alleviate various health issues. Herbs come in natural forms including roots, leaves, flowers, seeds and berries. Some herbal tea blends are designed to target multiple health conditions within the body.

Following are a few of my favourite herbal tea blend suggestions for some common health issues. If you can purchase all the herbs to create these blends that's great, but just using one or two of the listed herbs is still effective...

BEST DETOX BLEND for cleansing and purifying the blood, skin, liver and kidneys – *dandelion root, burdock, turmeric, red clover, ginger, liquorice root, nettle and oolong.*

BEST DIGESTION BLEND for poor digestion, IBS and stomach inflammation, which is gentle and soothing to the stomach after meals – *peppermint, fennel, fenugreek, hops, chamomile, ginger and spearmint.*

BEST BEDTIME BLEND to relax the central nervous system and overcome nervous anxiety and insomnia – *chamomile, lavender, rose petals, passionflower and valerian.*

BEST CLARITY AND STAMINA BLEND for supporting the adrenal glands and promoting memory and mental acuity – *lemon balm, rosemary, lemongrass, Siberian and Korean ginseng, ginkgo biloba and green tea.*

BEST SKIN ISSUES blend for soothing and calming inflamed and irritated skin, and alleviating skin conditions – *white tea, green tea, rosehips, lemongrass, milk thistle, calendula, chamomile, lavender and red clover.*

BEST ACNE BLEND is a therapeutic blend of liver supporting ingredients that detoxify and improve problem skin – *dandelion leaf, red clover, milk thistle and nettle.*

Best diabetes prevention blend to stabilise blood sugar levels, improve circulation and promote overall wellbeing – *tulsi leaf (holy basil), cinnamon, fenugreek and chamomile.*

Best immunity blend is a powerful combination of immunity boosting herbs that strengthen resistance to illness – *rosehips, ginger, lemongrass, Siberian ginseng, echinacea.*

Tea Party

Make up a number of invitations and invite several friends to your home for a Saturday afternoon tea party. Select a classic tea party theme like Alice in Wonderland or A Midsummer Night's Dream. Visit second-hand and charity stores to pick up a collection of mismatched teapots, teacups and tablecloths. Purchase an assortment of herbal teas and create some signature blends. Label and name your tea blends according to their origin and health benefits – these will be lovely gifts for your guests. Have plenty of candles, tea blossoms, fresh flowers, music to suit the theme, pillows and blankets. Opt to serve healthy foods of gourmet muffins, cakes, raw chocolates, gluten-free sandwiches, savoury tarts, mini pies and quiches. Imagine a feast for a king and place the delicious food high and low across a table, banquet style. Scatter the table with rose petals, glitter, jewels and playing cards. Ask your guests to contribute by bringing their favourite dish, with a recipe attached, to share with the other guests. Burn rose, frankincense and petitgrain essential oils to elevate the atmosphere of the tea party and encourage your precious guests to feel feminine, sophisticated and intellectually stimulated.

HOW DOES A HIPPY FIGHT A COLD?

"If there is no struggle, there will be no progress."

As the weather gets colder and our immunity is compromised, it is important to ensure we have the necessary remedies at hand to keep those winter blues at bay.

HERBAL TEA

When we have a cold nothing beats the highly warming and hydrating benefits of herbal tea. There are so many herbs that effectively alleviate nasal congestion, coughs and sore throats. The best are lemongrass, red clover, rosehips, Siberian ginseng, rosemary, thyme, ginger and clove. Drink four to six cups a day.

OLIVE LEAF EXTRACT

Used by hippies all over the world, olive leaf extract has a high antioxidant content making it great for reducing cold symptoms, lowering fevers and boosting immunity in times of illness. It is also good for cardiovascular health.

VITAMIN C

As if you don't remember those little tasty orange tablets you were given when you were little! These bad boys, known as vitamin C, are amazing for healing, repair and immunity. A regular intake of Vitamin C is always important but when you are sick it is crucial. Take 1000mg of the mighty C in supplement form and eat Vitamin C rich foods such as capsicums, zucchinis, broccoli, oranges, grapefruits and pineapples.

ZINC

This amazing mineral keeps the immune system strong and healthy. It drastically reduces both the duration and severity of all cold symptoms. When you have enough built up in your system it's impossible to even catch a cold. A good hippy will always have some practitioner grade liquid zinc hanging around the kitchen.

ELDERFLOWER AND ECHINACEA

Elderflowers have long been used to balance circulation and soothe inflammation of the nose, throat and eyes. Echinacea stimulates the production of white blood cells, making your body more capable of fighting viruses, colds, coughs, flu, and other respiratory illnesses. When you have a cold you can take these magical herbs in tea, powder, tincture or tablet form.

Organic onion, ginger and garlic

Three words: antibiotic, antibacterial and antiviral. My favourite sickness fighters, onion, ginger and garlic are all equally superb at killing harmful bacteria and getting rid of a nasty cold or flu. Eating garlic and ginger raw is best, however, eating them cooked is okay too. Before bed, tape a little of each to the soles of your feet. The drawing and healing benefits of this old trick are amazing for overcoming many chronic health conditions.

Green foods

When we are sick, the body's pH levels are disturbed. Eat like a true hippy and dose up on plenty of green tea, spinach, kale, avocado, olives and spirulina. These super green foods are marvellous for alkalising the body and maintaining a balanced pH level so the body can promptly heal and repair itself.

Hot spicy soups

Hot soups abundant in chilli, garlic, lemongrass, ginger, herbs and fresh vegetables are ideal for cleansing out a virus because of their antibiotic, antibacterial, hydrating and warming properties. Make your own or drag yourself to your local Thai or Vietnamese restaurant for a truly spicy soup experience.

Rosehips

Purchase some good quality dried rosehips and manuka honey, add two tablespoons of each to a small dish, cover the mixture with a little cold water then add some boiling water. Allow to sit for half a day, until the rosehips have softened and you can eat them. Rosehips are incredibly high in vitamin C, which is essential for repair, and manuka honey is Mother Nature's antibiotic elixir.

Essential oils

When hippies have a cold they add the pure essential oils of rosemary, eucalyptus, thyme, peppermint, sage, lavender and chamomile to a bowl of steaming hot water, cover their heads with a towel and inhale the relieving vapours for at least five minutes. Essential oils can also be used in an oil burner or vaporiser, and placed in a sick room, to cleanse the atmosphere and prevent others from becoming ill. These wonderful decongesting, calming essential oils are great for driving away any cold or flu symptoms.

Hot bath and water bottle

Prepare a hot water bottle and the hottest bath you can handle. Add one cup of Epsom salts, to your bath to get rid of toxins, and two drops of eucalyptus, and something warming like sandalwood, cedarwood or vetiver to clear the nose and soothe the lungs. When you are ready, get out and dry off, wrap yourself up in your warmest attire, have a glass of warm lemon water, grab the hot water bottle and get straight into bed. Sleep for eight hours and you'll be bright as a button when you wake up.

SAUNA

Save a sauna until the last stages of a cold, as you don't want to put unnecessary strain on the heart and lungs. A sauna or steam room is fantastic for clearing a lingering cold because you heat up and sweat it out. Sweating is very detoxifying. It removes germs and toxins from the body almost instantaneously. If you can think of other ways to work up a good sweat maybe you could try them too!

ONIONS IN THE ROOM

Cut two onions into quarters and place them beside your bed and around the bedroom when you have a cold or flu. This is an ancient remedy that draws the virus away from the ill person where it is absorbed and destroyed by the onion. It's a strange practice but it really works.

PROBIOTICS

To build a solid foundation for your immunity, a good place to start is where good health begins. In your digestive tract. Nurture the gut ecosystem with a daily probiotic supplement.

KARMA MAN

The law of cause and effect."

There is an unseen, powerful universal law called karma, the law of cause and effect where every thought, word and act carries an energy into the world and affects our future reality. The law of karma explains why each individual has a unique physical and mental disposition. If we do good things, good things will come to us. What we give out we get back. If we take, we will be taken from. Karma is neither judge nor jury, it just gives you the results of your actions. It's just a cosmic system that ensures we learn from our mistakes and rewards us for good behaviour. Karma is there to teach, not to punish. We are here on Earth to learn, and it is true that our karma provides the lessons.

Hip.

MACROBIOTIC

"Delicious meals begin with good quality produce, vision, imagination, intention and most importantly, love."

In macrobiotic philosophy you learn how to eat according to your body's needs, which depends on your individual constitution and current state of health. The four seasons and your overall wellbeing are always considered in macrobiotic cooking. When the adrenal glands and kidneys are low in energy, people feel worn out, overworked, emotionally depleted and upset. If you have these symptoms, it is advised you use a combination of organic pumpkin and adzuki beans in your cooking and eat little each day for one week. Eating a combination of these foods helps to restore kidney and adrenal health.

Pumpkin is fashionably chock-a-block full of vitamins, minerals, fibre, and antioxidants. Pumpkin agrees with most blood and body types' and gives a pleasing heartiness to both sweet and savoury meals. Adzuki beans, originally from Japan, are popular in soups and rice dishes, but can also be used in desserts. Like most beans, the adzuki bean is rich in soluble fibre which helps to eliminate cholesterol from the body. Adzuki beans are known for their healing properties and are particularly good for the kidneys, bladder and reproductive organs. The adzuki bean has a diuretic effect and has long been used to strengthen the kidneys.

Both pumpkin and adzuki beans are rich in magnesium, potassium, iron, zinc, copper, manganese and vitamin B3. Their high iron content makes them perfect food sources for vegetarians, particularly women. Try making a pumpkin, adzuki bean and brown rice stew using fresh vegetables, herbs and spices. Refrigerate and eat a little each day with every meal.

For more information and inspiration visit
WWW.KUSHIINSTITUTE.ORG

not having to do what everybody else does. Happiness , giving yourself the freedom to live your life exactly nt to."

Whatever made us think that cow's milk was a suitable choice for human consumption? The answer is that cow's milk is commercially convenient and people are conditioned to believe that it makes you healthy and strong.

The main purpose for drinking milk is to promote growth, something very necessary for children… but for adults? Humans are the only mammals that drink any kind of milk after weaning. They are also the only mammals that drink the milk of other mammals. Human beings are born with a thymus gland which excretes an enzyme necessary to digest milk. As we grow from childhood to adulthood, science shows us that this enzyme becomes virtually inactive.

Heating destroys the chief ingredient that helps us digest the protein and fats in milk. As most milk is homogenised and pasteurised, we don't really digest milk, nor obtain the nutrients from it. We can't get nutrients from food we don't digest. Because calcium is imperative for growth and the maintenance of strong and healthy teeth and bones, many people wonder how they will get the recommended daily intake if by not consuming milk, cheese and yoghurt. Almond and brazil nuts, soybeans, sesame seeds, tofu, green leafy vegetables, broccoli, parsley and seafood are all super high sources of calcium.

My mother drank two litres of cow's milk every day when she was pregnant with me. I have never broken a bone in my body. I respect cow's milk, and it has its benefits. However, the bottom line is there are now too many questions surrounding milk digestion, allergies, acne and the use of milk from cows that are treated with synthetic growth hormones.

ALTERNATIVES TO COW'S MILK ARE:

Soy milk

Soy milk is packed with protein, fibre and cancer fighting compounds. Be sure to drink only organic and non-GMO soy milk, because genetically engineered soy products are harmful to your health. Soy products should be used in moderation, as some experts suggest excessive soy may disturb thyroid and hormone levels.

Almond milk

Almond milk is another nutritional alternative to cow's milk that is rich in protein and a great source of magnesium, which helps to break down food into energy. It also provides manganese and phosphorus to the body and keeps the teeth and bones healthy. Soak your oats in almond milk overnight for a creamy, nutty bircher muesli.

Rice milk

Rice milk is fortified with niacin, vitamin B12, vitamin A, vitamin D and iron. Unlike cow's milk, rice milk doesn't contain lactose or cholesterol. This makes it good for your heart as well as a safe option for those who are lactose intolerant. Rice milk is sweet, making it a great milk to use in milkshakes.

Oat milk

Oat milk is cholesterol and lactose free, and contains roaring levels of the repairing antioxidant vitamin E. It also contains folic acid, which is essential for many bodily functions. Oat milk is great in coffee and insanely luscious in a malted iced coffee.

Quinoa milk

Quinoa milk has more calcium than cow's milk and is also a good source of iron, phosphorus, B vitamins and vitamin E. It has the added advantages of being an alkaline grain and is also gluten-free. The wonderful quinoa flavour meshes well with muesli, cereal and sprouted porridge, which contains grains and seeds that have been activated to release enzymes and nutritional properties.

Cashew milk

Cashews are a great source of magnesium, calcium and copper, making cashew milk an extremely valuable option for keeping our bones strong and healthy. Cashew milk blended with a little cinnamon and honey is heavenly, just like a glass of angel milk.

Always read the labels when shopping for milk substitutes and ensure all of the above are free from cane sugar, barley malt, rice syrup, artificial sweeteners, fructose and corn syrup. Added water, sea salt and sunflower oil are okay.

NATURE'S GATORADE

The coconut tree - also known as the tree of life."

The coconut, formally known as Cocos nucifera, is renowned over all the world for its refreshing taste and abundant healing properties. Coconut water is the liquid from young unripe coconuts and for centuries locals in tropical regions have been drinking it to boost immunity and vitality. I am always amazed by the way these cultures have consistently used food and natural remedies for healing without needing scientific evidence to prove their benefits; they seem to have an instinctive knowledge of what is healing for them.

Coconut water is rich in calcium, magnesium, sodium, phosphorus and potassium. These minerals are highly alkaline-forming, assisting the body's proper pH balance and metabolic function. In fact coconut water has a similar chemical composition to that of the human blood plasma. In WWII coconut water was injected into those in need of a blood transfusion. What a true gift of nature!

There is no beverage more hydrating and restoring than the cold water of the young coconut. And let me tell you, it is an absolute miracle cure for hangovers. Coconut water really cleanses the body of toxins, leaving you feeling restored and perfectly balanced. You can buy young coconuts at food markets, health food stores and supermarkets.

NOT TONIGHT HONEY

Thoughts lead to words, words lead to action, action leads to habit, habit leads to character, and character leads to providence."

Let's face it, headaches are a bitch! They say that every physical symptom our body presents is a reflection of our emotions, and headaches are said to be the cause of self-criticism and judgment. Just a little something to think about! Other causes of headaches can be dehydration, stress, poor sleep, neck tension, detoxing, magnesium deficiency and a diet high in artificial ingredients and preservatives. If you wake up with headaches or they become consistent and unbearable please see your doctor or naturopath.

HEADACHE REMEDIES:

PEPPERMINT AND LAVENDER ESSENTIAL OILS RUBBED INTO THE TEMPLES AND NECK – Along with a gentle self-temple massage, the use of peppermint and lavender essential oils will have an anti-inflammatory effect and assist with constricted blood vessels.

HALF A TEASPOON OF MAGNESIUM IN A GLASS OF PURIFIED WATER – Magnesium is a great mineral for alleviating headaches and muscular tension and for balancing the central nervous system.

WARM FOOTBATH CONTAINING EPSOM SALTS AND GREEN CLAY, AND A COLD FOREHEAD COMPRESS – Foot bathing has a detoxifying effect on the body, whilst the contrast of a cooling compress across the forehead is incredibly soothing.

LIE ON YOUR BACK WITH YOUR FEET UP THE WALL FOR IO MINUTES – A yoga posture to detoxify and improve circulation that will leave you feeling refreshed and balanced.

PRESS ALONG THE CRESCENTS UNDERNEATH YOUR EYEBROWS BACK AND FORTH – This is a favourite reflexology point for relieving head tension. Feels good, you should try it.

REFLEXOLOGY AND ACUPUNCTURE – Both these therapies are highly effective for relieving headaches as they treat the underlying causes.

A WARM ROSEMARY COMPRESS ACROSS THE FOREHEAD AND NECK – Rosemary has been used for centuries as a herbal remedy for headaches and poor circulation.

DEEP BREATHS AND FRESH AIR – This is the most effective way of getting fresh clean oxygen to your cells and blood. Learning to breathe properly could be just the trick to cure your headache.

AVOID ANY HEAVY OR ARTIFICIAL FOODS FOR A DAY – Poor diet is almost always the cause for all discomfort in the body. Give your system a rest and eat light, fresh, calming foods such as organic vegetable soups, fresh fruit, chamomile and peppermint tea for a day, and see how you feel. My friend Leyah once told me that a few slices of red capsicum can ease a headache. Try it, it works!

POVO

"Home cooking is the catalyst that brings a family together."

There are thousands of fast food outlets across Australia. They have increased in popularity in recent years due to their healthier choice menu options, which is a positive thing, as it confirms that people want to eat better. Fast food outlets tend to be an attractive option during tough economic times because they offer cheap deals that are quick, easy and appear to be value for money. This is an incorrect mentality. Value for money will always be home cooked meals that keep for a few days, feed the entire family and produce leftover ingredients from which to make other meals. Here is a list of personally tried and tested ingredients that will make breakfast, lunch, dinner and dessert for a week in tougher times all for under 70 dollars. The only catch is you have to make time to cook the meals and get a little imaginative with your creations – some suggestions would be stewed apple and sultana oat porridge; banana and honey crumble; red lentil and carrot soup; tuna, tomato and rice pilaf; Thai beef salad; zucchini and fetta quiche; brown rice, pumpkin and kidney bean stew; and banana, honey, yoghurt and soy milk smoothie. This kind of resourceful eating is much more economical and nutritionally sound than that any fast food outlet can offer. Shopping at farmers' markets and co-ops, and choosing the generic options from the supermarket is the cheapest way to purchase food.

1kg white or brown rice	1 bag tomatoes
1 bag rolled oats	1 Spanish onion
1 bag sultanas	4 bananas
1 bag red lentils	2 lemons
1 dozen free-range eggs	4 cans kidney, chickpea or butter beans
1 small jar honey	500g minute steak
1 bag carrots	200g delicatessen fetta cheese
1 pumpkin	1 garlic bulb
2 zucchinis	1 bottle cinnamon
1 cabbage	1 carton organic soy milk
1 iceberg lettuce	1 large tub Greek style natural yoghurt
1 bag apples	3 large cans dolphin safe tuna

PREGGERS

"A wise woman ought to realise that health is her most valuable possession."

The inability to conceive is often a medical mystery. We do know that endometriosis, pelvic inflammatory disease and stress can be obstacles to conception. Sometimes fate takes charge and it's necessary to wait for perfect timing. Medical science has been a blessing in providing medication and IVF support. But there are many cases where there is simply no solution and it becomes a waiting game. You can use primary procedures such as IVF and artificial insemination to get pregnant, but if the body's environment isn't healthy and balanced a foetus will not develop. Thankfully there are many holistic approaches to improving conditions for conception that have proven successful.

ACUPUNCTURE – The purpose of acupuncture is to nourish the organs and balance meridians, ensuring there is no disharmony in the body. Acupuncture has proven to be a highly effective modality for improving conditions necessary for pregnancy. It regulates the body's systems, stimulates the reproductive organs, and stabilises the hormone levels and sperm production in men.

HOLISTIC LIFESTYLE – If you wish to become pregnant begin by giving the body a complete clean up. Remove cigarettes, alcohol, drugs, caffeine, preservatives, artificial food, soft drinks and refined sugar from your life, and avoid all synthetic personal care products including toothpaste and deodorant containing aluminium. The cleaner and healthier your body is the more productively it functions.

HERBS – Herbs have been used to promote fertility for thousands of years. Be mindful that herbs can be very potent – it is important to speak with a registered herbalist before taking any herbal supplements. Personally I have found traditional Chinese herbs to have a profound effect when dealing with most health issues.

KINESIOLOGY – Kinesiology uses muscle testing to identify imbalances in the body's structural, chemical, emotional and energetic functions, and determine the body's healing needs. Kinesiology looks at the person as a whole, taking into account their psychological state, environment, physical body and chakras.

NUTRITION – Eat more organic foods including fresh fruit and vegetables, whole grains like brown rice, buckwheat, oatmeal, spelt, wild rice, soybeans, and zinc-rich foods such as oysters, tahini, pine nuts, lamb and pumpkin seeds. Choose foods high in vitamin C, like red capsicum, guava, broccoli and grapefruit. Calcium, vitamin D and B12 are said to encourage fertility in males and females.

ESSENTIAL OILS – Burn pure essential oils daily to relax your mind and encourage your connection to your higher self. I recommend lavender, mandarin, rose, cardamom, patchouli and ylang ylang because they help to balance the sacral chakra, too. Perhaps have an aromatherapist make you a massage blend you can use at home daily.

YOGA – Exercise helps to burn excess body fat, and balances hormone levels. It is best not to over exercise though – over exercising can actually impair fertility. Yoga is the perfect exercise to promote fertility, as it is fairly gentle and great for balancing the body and mind. Certain yoga positions are referred to as fertility poses because they are thought to help stimulate hormone production, and increase blood flow to the reproductive organs.

RITUAL

"If you don't go after what you want, you'll never have it. If you don't step forwards you're always in the same place."

Looking after your body and mind is probably the most important thing you can do to develop a better relationship with yourself. It is always what I spend the most time and money on. I strongly believe that your body is your biggest investment, and if we plan on sticking around we must do our very best to look and feel our best! I would like to share with you my health and beauty rituals, but ssshhhhh it's top secret; we don't want everyone knowing how to look smoking hot, now, do we?

MORNING RITUAL

LEMON AND APPLE CIDER VINEGAR – Upon waking have a large glass of warm filtered water with either fresh lemon juice or apple cider vinegar. It helps to promote digestion and liver function. The vitamin C in lemons also helps the body burn fat.

MEDITATE – We all talk about it, we are all inquisitive about those grounded people we meet that say they practise it, but we just never seem to find the time to actually do it. Create a space in your bedroom, put on some relaxing music, light a candle, and dedicate five minutes to sitting on a pillow. Simply breathe and become present.

STRETCH – Just like cats do! In Ayurvedic medicine it is encouraged for all body types to commence the day with a few basic stretches; touch your toes, roll your wrists and ankles and do some side and back bends. This awakens the muscles, supplies fluid to the joints and fresh blood to the cells. A mobile body is a happy and energised one, and you will quickly notice a difference in your energy levels.

AROMATHERAPY – Begin the day using energising and stimulating lime, rosemary, orange, grapefruit and mandarin pure essential oils. Incorporate these fresh citrus aromas into your morning by burning them in an oil burner, using them in a shower gel, or moisturise with a signature body oil that has an almond oil base.

COFFEE – Organic coffee is incredibly stimulating for the mind and body, promoting mental clarity and digestion. Use a stainless steel espresso maker and enjoy as the gorgeous aroma fills the room. Almond milk, cinnamon and honey in coffee is delicious.

BREAK THE FAST – Breakfast is a particularly important time of the day to be extra selective about what you put in your body, because you're ending the fast from dinner the night before. Your cells are hungry, clean, and primed to rapidly absorb whatever you throw at them. Start the day with foods that are savoury, alkalising and cleansing so you feel energised and your blood sugar levels are balanced. Lightly stir-fried green vegetables with fish and brown rice is perfect.

DRY SKIN BRUSHING – Before showering use a dry skin brush to help eliminate toxins and skin congestion; start at the soles of your feet and firmly brush upwards, focusing on the legs, butt, stomach and the back of the arms.

TONGUE SCRAPING – The ancient Ayurvedic healing philosophy of India has recommended tongue scraping for centuries to aid digestion, a healthy mouth and clear sinuses. Cleaning the salivary glands helps to activate and enhance digestion. Purchase a tongue scraper online or from a dental clinic.

ORGANIC SKINCARE – Make the switch to organic make-up and skincare products. These commodities are kinder to your body and the environment. Synthetic skincare is full of toxic petrochemicals, artificial and harmful ingredients which are absorbed directly into the body, resulting in mineral toxicity and poor health.

PRE-PARTY RITUAL

DAY OF LIGHT FOODS – Before a special party or event, spend a day or two only eating fresh fruits, salads and steamed vegetables. Easily digestible foods allow the body to heal, cleanse and repair. A rested and clean body reflects in bright eyes, glowing skin and shiny hair. If you're lucky your tummy might get a little flatter too!

MOVEMENT – Engage in some gentle exercise before the event, like a beach walk or yoga class. This promotes mental clarity and energy flow throughout the body, leaving you feeling flexible and energised for a night of fun.

AROMATHERAPY – Burn pure essential oils in your home, while you get ready for the occasion. This will balance, restore, enhance your confidence and sensuality. Try geranium, neroli, jasmine, ylang ylang and rose. By smelling these oils you will feel centred, ready to have fun and engage deeply with others.

TEA BAGS – Place two black or green tea bags in a saucer of water and put in the freezer for five minutes. Then, lie down and place them on your eyelids for 10 minutes to eliminate puffiness and dark circles. Enjoy the cooling tea bags and put your legs up the wall to promote further circulation and vitality.

HYDRATION – Skin health requires hydration in the form of fresh water, pure coconut water, fresh juice and herbal tea. Pre-party spend the day sipping on hydrating liquids to ensure a glowing and clear complexion.

SAND SALT SCRUB – Make up your own body scrub and polish your precious skin using either sand, poppy seeds or ground rock salt. Add half a cup of olive oil to one cup of chosen exfoliant and scrub away from head to toe in a circular motion. Rinse with warm water and apply your favourite body oil.

SEX HAIR – Make a hair treatment using jojoba and coconut oil, smooth through damp hair and leave for one hour before thoroughly shampooing. Once hair is clean and blow-dried, smooth out with a fine film of coconut oil to add a glossy shine and a luscious aroma.

NIGHT TIME RITUAL

AMBIENCE – The evening is a time for reflection, peace and rest. Create an atmosphere of tranquillity, by burning pure essential oils, playing peaceful music and illuminating your home with lamps. Calm down in a space that is tranquil, clean and comfortable.

DINNER TIME – Always eat a light and wholesome dinner early. Salads, soups, vegetarian stews and roasted vegetables are all good dinner choices. Eat lightly so your body can easily digest its food before repairing and detoxifying whilst you sleep.

BEDTIME BEVERAGE – Half an hour after dinner make a cup of chamomile, peppermint and lavender tea. This will aid digestion and deeply relax you before sleep. These herbs also help with skin irritations and red eyes. For babies and children, chamomile tea brewed in rice milk is a perfect blend.

AROMATHERAPY – Before sleep, vaporise, self-massage or have a long bath in a combination of clary sage, lavender, rose, frankincense, neroli and chamomile pure essential oils. These aromas greatly assist with deep relaxation and leave you feeling blissful and serene.

FOOT RINSE – Always cleanse your feet and hands before prayer and sleep. A footbath containing lavender and peppermint essential oil is perfect. Rinsing the hands and feet is a hygienic practice of washing away the daily dirt, and is also symbolic of cleansing away the day's emotions. Finish by applying a natural aromatherapy foot and hand lotion.

BEDTIME – It is said that the best quality sleep occurs before midnight. Aim to get ready for slumber before 10pm at least three nights per week, even if this means sipping on herbal tea, resting and reading in bed. A bedroom is not a room for a television, a computer or video games. A bedroom is a relaxing space with soft lighting, a mellow tone and comfortable furniture.

SEASONAL LIVING

"Improve your health by learning to live in harmony with nature and the four seasons."

The rhythms of the seasons are viewed by many ancient civilisations as important phases for the wellbeing of human beings. We can better understand the meaning of life through a deeper connection to the rhythms of nature. There are positive things you can do during each season to connect with the environment and flow of the Earth's cycles.

SPRING – AN OPPORTUNITY FOR DYNAMIC GROWTH AND INSPIRATION

Spring is a time for new beginnings and development. In nature animals are born, flowers bloom and plant life is green, fresh and abundant, making spring the perfect season to start sowing seeds in your life, following through with ideas and implementing changes. Clean and detox your home and personal life. Because spring is traditionally a time for cleansing, your spring diet should contain more liver and gallbladder cleansing foods including green leafy salads, seaweed, lightly stir-fried vegetables, fresh herbs, bitter and sour soups. Start the day with some fresh green juice and sip on dandelion tea throughout the day. Throughout the spring season duration burn pure essential oils of rosemary, grapefruit, coriander, basil and geranium to help manifest your ideals and dreams.

SUMMER – THE SEASON FOR SETTING YOURSELF FREE

The summer months are a time of personal fulfilment and vitality. The season brings long, warm days for enjoyment and celebration. In life we must celebrate our sacrifices and achievements. Summer time is about acknowledging the abundance and individual freedom. Summer is also a good time to lose weight. A lighter diet of fresh fruits, clear soups, long grain rice, quinoa salads and seafood is ideal. Go bushwalking, swimming and take brisk beach walks. During summer our senses become heightened and our passion for life and people is aroused. They don't call it summer lovin' for nothing! Express your love and free your heart by burning the playful aromas of ylang ylang, vanilla, rose, orange and lime essential oils.

AUTUMN – A TIME FOR HARVEST AND INNER BALANCE

Traditionally autumn is a season to stock up and gather food supplies in preparation for the cold winter months. It's a great time to nurture the physical body and attend to health issues that may require attention. Use this time to discover your purpose in life and how you balance your personal needs with your commitments in the outside world. As the autumn leaves fall, shed some of your old habits. When the weather becomes cooler enjoy more protein-based meals, that include organic meat, tofu and legumes, and make soups and stews that are abundant in pumpkin, sweet potatoes and carrots. Embrace the crisp autumn afternoons by taking long walks in nature. Capture the enchanting spirit of autumn by burning pine, nutmeg, frankincense and bergamot essential oils.

WINTER – A RESTFUL PERIOD OF TRANQUILLITY AND PEACE

Winter is a time to relax, recuperate and reflect. Many people find they are challenged with seasonal affective disorder (SAD) in winter. Find your happiness by doing pleasant things for yourself, talking with friends, having long hot baths and eating delicious food. A diet that allows you to build energy is ideal. Eat hearty meats, vegetable soups, casseroles, baked dinners, porridge and hot drinks. Stay warm, physically challenged and energised by practising vinyasa and Bikram yoga. Burning pure essential oils of frankincense, cedar wood, lavender and sandalwood will help you see the light during the darker times and encourage you to appreciate the beauty and stillness of winter.

SECRET GARDEN

"I listen to the needs of others, I respect everybody I meet and coexist in harmony."

Many health practitioners say that disease starts in the gut. The digestive system is the foundation of your health, as it is 70 per cent of your immune system. You can take all the supplements and vitamins in the world, but if your foundation is not right, then it's pointless because you won't absorb nutrients if your gut health is out of balance.

Think of your body as a lush, healthy, clean and fragrant garden that needs to be tended. It wants to be moist, alive with greenery and obtain a perfect balance of sun and shade. If you would like a healthy body, the digestive system must be balanced and maintained.

Poor digestive health is generally the result of what we put in our mouth. Bad eating habits directly contribute to poor gut health. The more nutritious the food, the better your gut will feel. Clean up your garden, and throw out all the rubbish including drugs, alcohol, cigarettes, refined and processed food and drinks.

When your soil is clean and tidy, speak to a naturopath about taking a beneficial bacteria of lactobacillus rhamnosus, lactobacillus acidophilus and bifidobacterium lactis. A live blood test and hair mineral analysis is a good idea if you feel unsure as to what you might be lacking in your diet or uncertain about the level of toxicity in your body. Hair mineral analysis measures the amount of minerals stored in your body. It's also an effective way to monitor toxic metals in the body such as lead, cadmium, mercury and arsenic.

SKINNY BITCH

An unnamed famous model once said... "Nothing tastes as good, as looking skinny feels."

I'm not quite sure I agree, but I do know that it feels amazing to have a lean and healthy figure. Long term weight loss will not be achieved by skipping meals, starving yourself or going on weird random diets. Weight loss is only successful if your metabolism and digestive system function properly, and they can only do this if you eat. Small, regular, healthy, well balanced meals ensure your body has a consistent supply of energy to burn. Practise the magical method of portion control as weight gain comes from too much fat, too much protein, too many calories, and too much of everything! Each day, aim to have a little functional fat, some lean plant or animal protein, a small amount of complex carbohydrates and just a bit of natural sugar. Eating late at night when your body slows down for rest is not a good idea. Eating a savoury, high protein breakfast kick starts the metabolism, and should therefore never be missed.

Your metabolism basically controls how fast your body deals with anything that passes through it, including food, drink and toxins. The faster your metabolism is, the better you'll be able to process these things. A quicker metabolism means that your body will absorb any food you eat faster, and you'll gain its energy benefits more effectively. Exercise is your metabolism's best friend; the body just loves to work hard to get the metabolic rate happening! Sorry to break it to you, but moving your butt every day is the only way to do this. Exercise should be looked at positively. We all know it feels amazing; it's our mind that actually stops us from committing to regular exercise. Do whatever exercise you enjoy or fits into your life – walk to work, make love every day, play a team sport, lift weights, box, or hit the gym. Regular massages, saunas, plenty of sleep and purified water are all additional ways to enhance weight loss.

THE TOP METABOLIC BOOSTING HELPERS ARE:

WATER – Drinking water actually speeds up weight loss and boosts metabolism. Because we often mistake thirst for hunger, when you think you are hungry have a glass of water and see if you're still feeling hungry in five minutes time.

CHILLI AND SPICY STUFF – Spicy foods speed up metabolism, curb your cravings, and give you energy. Eating chilli generates heat in the body, which helps to burn more calories after a meal. Add fresh or dried chilli flakes to your meals as often as possible.

GINGER – Ginger has a positive effect on the human digestive system. Eating ginger increases your metabolic rate, helping you break down fatty foods and proteins to be used by the body.

GREEN TEA – Green tea has a massive impact on your metabolism, because it is super high in antioxidants and has a small amount of caffeine. Consuming antioxidants means you will have stronger skin cells, better functioning liver and kidneys, and a faster metabolism.

CAYENNE PEPPER – The active ingredient in cayenne pepper is the compound capsaicin, which is responsible for raising the metabolism by positively affecting proteins that help break down fat.

SEAWEED – The iodine in seaweed helps regulate metabolism. Iodine is an essential element for the production of thyroid hormones, which affect metabolic rate. Seaweeds are also packed with energy-boosting B vitamins and minerals that fight stress and fatigue so you stay active and energised.

SEAFOOD – Seafood is abundant in high quality proteins that help to speed up the metabolism, helping you maintain a healthy weight. They also protect against overweight-related complications, such as diabetes, cardiovascular disease and strokes.

LEMON AND LIME – Lemons and limes are rich in citric acid. By having a glass of lemon or lime juice in purified warm water first thing in the morning you introduce a natural digestive aid into your stomach. The pectin in these fruits, mops up fats and interacts with the other acids and enzymes in the body which contributes to a well functioning digestive system.

OATS – Starting the day with a bowl of oats makes you feel fuller and supplies you with energy, which helps with weight loss. The soluble fibre in oats slows down digestion, spreading the rise in blood sugar over a longer time period.

Apple cider vinegar – Have 10ml of apple cider in 15ml of water twice a day, 10 minutes before meals to increase your metabolism and burn body fat. Apple cider vinegar is a genius remedy that can lower blood sugar levels so it is beneficial for those with type one and two diabetes. It also counteracts water retention because it regulates water content in cells and flushes sodium from the body.

Coconut oil – One food that can kick start your metabolism even more than protein is coconut oil. Raw virgin coconut oil helps to normalize the thyroid gland, and the thyroid gland is one of the key organs responsible for controlling the speed of your metabolism. A perfectly functioning thyroid helps the body convert fats into energy more effectively. Consuming coconut oil increases energy levels, lessens cravings for carbohydrates and sugar, and leaves you feeling satisfied.

Apples – Eat an apple before meals as the fibre in apples makes you feel full and the sweetness satisfies sugar cravings. The pectin in apples reduces absorption of cholesterol both in the blood and liver, and the polyphenols in apples prevent the oxidation of cell membrane fats.

Pineapple – Eating pineapples helps to improve digestion by breaking down proteins in the digestive tract. Pineapples promote weight loss due to their enzymatic action. They also prevent inflammation and swelling, resulting in a healthy functioning digestive system.

SLEEP EASY

The best way to overcome despair and worry is to have a good night's sleep; problems always look smaller after a warm meal and a good night's sleep."

Troubles with sleep are common. Sleep deprivation is a frustrating, and depleting experience and it most certainly affects your appearance and performance. The cause of insomnia is a mixed bag of many contributing factors – the usual culprits are stress, an overactive mind, poor diet, toxicity, health and environment problems. Sleep is the time when your body renews and replenishes itself, repairing damage caused by stress, toxicity and environmental pollution.

MAGNESIUM – A magnesium deficiency can contribute to sleep problems. As most people are magnesium deficient, visit a naturopath to check your magnesium and calcium levels, and if required, take a supplement from the health food store. Indulging in a warm bath containing Epsom salts or magnesium sulphate, is a good way to relax the muscles and calm the nervous system.

AROMATHERAPY – Using pure essential oils in an oil burner, bath or massage can greatly help overcome sleep problems. Lavender, neroli, chamomile, orange and geranium are ideal for calming the nervous system, easing stress and promoting relaxation.

SET THE SCENE – Atmosphere is everything; it's all about the vibe man! When it comes to evening ambience you need warm cosy lighting, plush organic cotton bedlinen, candles and a calm and still bedroom to host the important occasion of sleep. Atmosphere should be beautiful for all life's activities.

ELIMINATION – Remove stimulants such as coffee, black tea, chocolate and refined sugars from your diet if you have trouble sleeping. If you are not clear of stimulants then you are not giving your body and mind an adequate chance to relax and wind down.

SLEEPY FOODS – Nature provides us with nutritious foods that also stimulate production of serotonin and melatonin, the hormones responsible for good sleep.

- BANANAS – Bananas have high levels of melatonin and serotonin, and magnesium, which are all effective at promoting relaxation and sleep.

- CHERRIES – Cherries are one of the few food sources of melatonin, the chemical that regulates sleep.

- OATMEAL WITH HONEY – Oats are rich in melatonin, as well as zinc selenium and magnesium. Eating a bowl of oatmeal and honey activates insulin production, raising blood sugar naturally and making you feel sleepy. Honey is a natural relaxant and has been used for centuries in Traditional Chinese Medicine for insomnia and calming the nervous system.

- ALMONDS AND CASHEWS – Almonds and cashews are full of essential vitamins and minerals that calm the central nervous system. They both contain an amino acid that acts as a sedative - and magnesium, an effective muscle relaxant.

MEDITATION – The regular practice of meditation creates the conditions necessary for life to fall perfectly into place. Through meditation we quieten the chatter of the mind, and get to know our higher self. Sleepless nights dissipate when the fluctuations of the mind cease.

EXERCISE – Daily exercise is important, as physical movement allows the body to perform its functions more effectively. Choose an activity you enjoy like yoga, bush walking, tennis or a few simple stretches on the beach.

HERBAL MEDICINE – Calming herbal teas such as chamomile, peppermint, lavender, hops, valerian and passionflower are great for assisting with sleep problems. A cup of chamomile, valerian and passionflower tea before bed, will put you straight to sleep.

JOURNALING – Before bedtime, write a list of tomorrow's tasks to get the thoughts off your mind. Put today's worries onto a piece of paper and then let it go. Write down tomorrow's agenda and deal with it tomorrow. What's done is done, and what is yet to come is not yet your concern. All we have is now, so enjoy the present.

SO WHAT'S THE STORY WITH AROMATHERAPY FOOD?

"Food should do so much more than just feed your body. It should feed your soul."

The concept of utilising food as a remedy has been around for thousands of years and today science has proven the many health benefits of a diet that includes vitamins, spices, minerals, fibre, protein, amino acids and antioxidants. Pure essential oils are the highly concentrated extracts of fruits, seeds, herbs, flowers, barks, leaves and roots. When cooking with pure essential oils you add medicinal value to the meal; be mindful that you should only use 100 per cent certified organic pure essential oils.

Aromatherapy food is fragrant, real, nurturing, creative and nutritionally sound. You will notice all my recipes are enriched with many types of aromatherapy food, ranging from fresh herbs and spices, to a drop of an essential oil here and there. Most importantly, when you begin to cook like this, you will discover, your food becomes so much more than food, it becomes an artwork.

My true appreciation for aromatherapy food began one evening in December 2008 at a Nepalese restaurant. The occasion was a work Christmas function so we ordered pretty much everything on the amazing menu. Nepalese food is incredibly fragrant, healthy and can be really diverse. At some point in the evening my boss Salvatore Battaglia, author of *The Complete Guide to Aromatherapy*, lent across the table and said, "Wow Rita, this food is fantastic, it's like aromatherapy food." I looked down to honour the flavours and I recall seeing an array of colour, the greenest coriander, ruby red chilli, woods of garlic, giant sized eggplant and perfect mushrooms all soaking in a slightly lemon yellow pool of coconut milk. It became apparent to me what aromatherapy food is; when you eat fresh herbs and spices it's almost as if you're cold pressing them in your mouth, releasing an abundance of essential nutrients, aromas and phenomenal flavours. This type of food is indeed aromatherapy food.

SOMETHING TO DIGEST

"Happiness does not mean that everything is perfect. It just means you have decided to look beyond the imperfections."

A healthy digestive system will take you places baby! No honestly, on a serious note it is crucial that we all maintain a well functioning digestive system, as this ensures the nutrients from the food we eat are absorbed to their full potential. Good digestive function is so crucial to immunity because a very high percentage of the immune system is located in the gut.

Digestive problems are among the most common health problems in the world today. The presenting symptoms are irritable bowel syndrome (IBS), constipation, gas, peptic ulcers, nausea, reflux and diarrhoea. The result of impaired digestion is generally due to a lack of digestive enzymes and nutrients, food allergies, poor diet, and prescription drugs. Food that is not digested properly ferments in the intestinal tract causing gas, bloating, weight gain and abdominal pain. If you suspect a certain food is upsetting your digestive system, avoid it for a few days to see if your digestion improves.

THE THINGS THAT PROMOTE DIGESTION ARE:

- Have 10ml of apple cider vinegar in 10ml of water before and after meals
- Plan meal times according to the Chinese body clock
- Drink lemon in warm water first thing in the morning
- Avoid drinking fluids with meals
- Have one drop of pure peppermint essential oil in a glass of lukewarm water 15 minutes after a meal
- Take a practitioner grade probiotic
- Take acidophilus capsules
- Chew your food thoroughly and mindfully
- Take a vitamin B-complex supplement
- Go for a daily walk
- Eat only soups, brown rice and salads one day a week
- Burn fennel, peppermint and spearmint pure essential oils

SPIRULINA – THE SUPER FOOD

"It tastes a little suss, but go on, drink it anyway."

This tiny sea plant has been eaten by humans since prehistoric times. Today it is harvested worldwide as a super food. Imagine a vegetable with more protein than tofu, more vitamin A than carrots, more iron than red meat, that is also a sensational source of protective phytochemicals, and you have spirulina.

Spirulina is a rich source of chlorophyll, which is awesome for removing toxins from the body, including heavy metals, cleansing the bowel, liver and bloodstream. All green leafy vegetables contain chlorophyll, but none have as much as spirulina. The nutritional data on spirulina is profound. It is truly a powerhouse of health, containing vitamins E, B1, B2, B6, B12, biotin, pantothenic acid, folic acid, inositol, niacin and the carotenoids necessary for vitamin A production. It is also abundant in minerals, including potassium, calcium, magnesium, manganese, zinc, selenium, iron and phosphorus.

Spirulina's reputation as a super food is notably due to its proven properties as a complete nutritional source; basically it's got everything the body needs, not just to work, but to work well. Today you can buy organic spirulina in capsule, liquid and powder form, from health food stores and chemists. Personally I drink the powdered form as I feel it is absorbed best. You can add it to purified water, juice or smoothies – just get it in your guts!

SPIRULINA SAUCE

1 tsp spirulina powder
½ tsp cayenne pepper
1 cup raw macadamias
½ cup purified water

Place all the ingredients into a blender and process for two minutes or until smooth. The spirulina sauce will keep refrigerated in a glass airtight jar for a week and can be added to salads, boiled eggs, fried tofu, steamed vegetables and breads.

SWEET ENOUGH

There is an underlying reason why people crave sugar. We crave it for comfort in a world that scares us, to push down our emotions and temporarily feel better."

Of all the unhealthy things we should ditch, refined sugar is at the top of the list. Sugar is toxic death for the body. The human body is not designed to process refined sugar. Give it up and you are promised weight loss, smoother digestion, relaxed muscles, less confusion, more peaceful emotions and increased mental clarity.

Refined sugar has absolutely no nutritional benefits. It weakens the immune system, depletes skin collagen levels and pollutes the body in every way. There are many natural sweeteners that can replace refined sugar, which you can use in coffee, tea and baking. In fact you can use a natural sweetener in all cooking of any dish that requires sugar. Other alternatives to sugar include:

DRIED FRUITS, SUCH AS DATES, PRUNES, FIGS, SULTANAS AND RAISINS – They are sweet and full of dietary fibre, vitamins and minerals. Dried fruits can be used in jam, muffins, cakes and savoury stews.

FRESH FRUITS LIKE PINEAPPLES, APPLES, APRICOTS AND PEACHES – Fresh fruits are naturally sweet and packed full of vitamins. They are also cleansing and easy to digest. Pineapple, apples, apricots and peaches are delicious in desserts, salads, muffins, slices and cakes.

PRUNE, POMEGRANATE OR PEAR JUICE CONCENTRATE – Juice concentrates are rich in antioxidants and dietary fibre that supports superior bowel health. Add fruit concentrates to sweet sauces, marinades, muesli and granola.

STEVIA – A naturally sweet herb, stevia helps to lower blood pressure, aid digestion and reduce gas and stomach acidity. Use stevia powder in tea and coffee instead of sugar. Stevia comes in liquid and powdered form and it can be used in any dish that requires sweetness.

RAW, UNPROCESSED CANE SUGAR – Raw or unrefined sugar is cane juice that has been minimally processed, unlike white sugar, which has been robbed of its nutrients. Use as an alternative to white sugar in tea, coffee and baking.

PALM SUGAR – Made from the sap of the sugar palm tree, this nectar of the gods delivers the perfect sweetness to curries, sauces, syrups and desserts.

Rapadura sugar – Unlike white sugar, rapadura sugar is an unrefined sugar that has high nutritional value because it retains most of its natural vitamins and minerals. Use when making chocolates, puddings and sauces.

Demerara sugar – This unrefined sugar is completely free of harmful chemicals and has a rich and creamy flavour, making it appropriate for hot and cold beverages and a number of baking recipes.

Coconut sugar – Coconut sugar comes from the buds of coconut tree flowers. It is perfect for baking delicious treats like cookies and apple crumble because the texture of coconut sugar is similar to that of white sugar.

Pure grape juice – Pure grape juice is high in antioxidants and is a wonderful sugar substitute. It adds interesting flavour to both meaty stews and sweet desserts.

Agave syrup – Agave syrup has a much lower glycaemic index than sugar, which means the slower the rise in blood sugar levels when it is consumed. The syrup of agave gives a moist texture to baked foods. It is great for brownies and banana bread.

Rice malt syrup – Rice malt syrup is made by culturing rice with enzymes to break down the starches and then it is cooked until it becomes syrup. It has a mild sugary flavour and can be used to sweeten most dishes.

Maple syrup – Made from the sap of maple trees, maple syrup contains many trace minerals and is ideal for Asian style stir-fries and caramelising onions and nuts.

Raw honey – Raw honey is the ultimate natural healing remedy and a great sweetener for cooking and baking because it adds flavour and provides many health benefits. Raw honey is antiviral, antifungal and has anti-cancer properties.

It is important to know that naturally sweet foods provide us with high-quality vitamins and minerals. As long as we balance the sweet tastes with the other four tastes that are sour, bitter, salty and pungent, according to Traditional Chinese Medicine, we will maintain good health. By using only natural and unrefined sweeteners we can help bring sugar addictions under control. However, you'll still need a little willpower to rebalance your body's cravings.

⟨ KRISHNA FOR THE HARE FOOD

d negative karmic influences which result from violence."

Some of the most wholesome food I have ever eaten, without a doubt, has been Hare Krishna cuisine. It tastes so good and you feel nourished and calm after eating it. The main contenders on a Hare Krishna menu are home-made vegetarian curries, kofta balls, rice and halva pudding. Everyone loves Hare Krishna food, and the Hare Krishnas love everybody!

The Hare Krishna people live on food that's natural, cheap and tastes sensational because they respect the Earth and its creatures. Their way of eating has been enjoyed physically and spiritually for centuries.

Hare Krishna people have a beautiful reputation for feeding the world. The Hare Krishna Food For Life program feeds people worldwide for free!

Visit WWW.FFL.ORG for more details.

THE CAVE MAN DIET

"The reason why some of us don't care about what we put in to our bodies is either we don't understand the body or we don't appreciate it."

The cave man hunter-gatherer style diet includes organic fruits, vegetables, lean meat, poultry, seafood, nuts, seeds, sprouts, eggs, whole grains, plant oils and absolutely nothing artificial or processed. After all, our ancestors did not consume preservatives and artificial foods, and these are also the people who survived to procreate our current population, didn't they?

Western societies have a shocking reputation for what they eat. Packaged, canned and microwave meals are considered to be acceptable mealtime options in the west. Processed, preserved, refined and additive packed foods are a daily choice for many, yet we sit and wonder why we battle with health problems such as headaches, arthritis, diabetes, skin conditions, allergies, cancer, high blood pressure, heart disease, strokes, behavioural problems, depression and insomnia. Although awareness is increasing, it is still surprising that so many people fail to recognise the link between good food and good health. Synthetic or processed foods create conditions that disrupt balance leading to many human physical and psychological problems.

The answer is simple. We are what we eat. A poor diet results in disease. If you want to feel healthy and live a life free from suffering, then only eat good food. Basically our body, the vehicle in which we exist, does not understand food that is unnatural. I'm sure our ancestors—the Aboriginals, Aztecs and Native American Indians—were not pouring cream on their cooked goanna, or garnishing buffalo with bottled sauce.

Today modern society embraces the Paleo diet. To find out more about this dietary system please visit
WWW.ULTIMATEPALEOGUIDE.COM

THE GOAT VS THE COW

"Joyful thoughts strengthen your body, revive your spirit and gladden the heart. Joyful thoughts empower and balance your being."

Goat's and cow's milk are nutritionally similar, yet structurally different. The main difference is that goat's milk is easier to digest because the fat molecules are smaller than those in cow's milk. For this reason consuming goat's milk instead of cow's milk reduces the possibility of allergies, asthma, indigestion and other ailments. Goat's milk contains more calcium, vitamin B6, vitamin A, potassium, niacin, copper, phosphorous, manganese and selenium than cow's milk.

Personally I'm not a huge fan of making my body work any harder than it has to. For years I suffered fatigue and digestive problems. The body should not have to struggle; if our system struggles to digest something it makes me think it just doesn't want or need what is making it struggle. After I switched to goat and sheep's milk products, my energy levels rapidly increased and I seriously felt lighter within my body. Like goat's milk, sheep's milk has small fat globules that are easily digested; both these products are a rich source of iodine, which is helpful for those with thyroid problems. You can buy goat and sheep's milk alternatives in the form of yoghurt, cheese and milk.

It is important to choose fresh, organic and unpasteurized whole milk. Ayurveda teaches to drink warm milk with a pinch of clove, ginger and saffron to promote digestive fire.

THE INCONVENIENT TRUTH

"The truth is beautiful, because it's true."

Is margarine better than butter? No, it's a tragic myth! Butter is a completely natural food that contains natural health benefits and margarine is a synthetic product made from toxic chemicals with zero nutritional value. It has been suggested that margarine is biochemically just one molecule away from plastic and shares 27 ingredients with paint. Margarine and other hydrogenated, processed polyunsaturated oils contain trans fatty acids and other synthetic ingredients that undermine cell health which leads to disease. People originally began using margarine because it was marketed as a low fat alternative to butter and for this reason it is said to be healthier. In fact butter has been around for centuries, and in small amounts, is quite good for you as it helps the body absorb other nutrients in food. Your body will never understand margarine for the simple reason that it is not natural.

People need to ditch the false belief that high-quality plant oils, nuts and seeds should be avoided because they are high in fat. The consumption of good fats is highly important because we need essential fatty acids in our diet to promote healthy, youthful skin and hair, growth and energy, to support thyroid and adrenal function, as well as healthy blood, nerves and arteries. Essential fatty acids are also necessary for the proper functioning of the immune system. It is my mission in life to help people to understand it is far better for your health to eat something natural that is higher in fat, than something that is synthetic claiming to be low in fat. In the same way it is better to have natural sugar such as honey and a natural fat like olive oil, than to have a toxic sugar-free or fat-free chemical additive.

HIGHLY NUTRITIOUS ALTERNATIVES TO MARGARINE THAT CAN BE FOUND IN SUPERMARKETS AND HEALTH FOOD STORES ARE:

BUTTER – Occasionally indulge in a tub of organic butter. The origin of butter goes back thousands of years. It is a rich source of vitamin A, which is necessary for thyroid and adrenal function.

TAHINI – Tasty tahini is made from hulled or ground sesame seeds making it abundant in protein and vitamin A. It is a highly nutritious spread and sauce option.

GHEE – Clarified butter is a traditional staple in Indian cooking. Ghee nourishes the skin, aids digestion, and helps the body assimilate nutrients.

NUTTELEX AND PLANT STEROL SPREADS – These are usually made from sunflower or olive oils, and are dairy-free but similar in texture to butter. Great for vegans and those allergic to dairy.

OLIVE, COCONUT AND SUNFLOWER OILS – Use any of these three oils in their cold pressed and raw form. Simply pour and smear them across sweet and savoury breads, cakes and muffins.

PURE MACADAMIA, ALMOND, PEANUT, OR CASHEW BUTTERS – Decadent and delicious, these nut butters are packed with unsaturated fats, vitamins and minerals that help to lower cholesterol. In moderate amounts, nut butters do not compromise the waistline.

HUMMUS – Made from chickpeas, olive oil, tahini and lemon juice, hummus is an exceptionally healthy food that tastes heavenly. It contains protein and cholesterol-lowering essential fatty acids.

GOAT CURD – Goat cheese is an excellent alternative to cream cheese and butter. Goat curd is rich in vitamins and minerals and is delicious spread upon thick seeded bread, and followed by jams and chutneys.

AVOCADO – This super fruit is remarkably creamy, making it a moreish addition to lots of different meals. Avocados are particularly rich in essential fatty acids, potassium, folate and vitamin E, making them great for the skin and general health.

THE BUSY LIVER

"The liver is our centre of courage and resoluteness - if it is in a state of good health."

The liver is believed to be the organ of longevity. I would like to tell you a little bit about your liver, why you should love it, look after it and most of all listen to it.

- The cells within the liver contain a number of powerful enzymes that break down the many toxins and chemicals that can be found in some of the things we eat.

- Alcohol is processed in the liver.

- The liver creates bile that breaks down fats; bile is stored in the gallbladder.

- The liver filters the blood and helps remove harmful chemicals and bacteria from the body.

- The liver stores vitamins, minerals and sugars.

- The liver is the body's detoxifier and the second largest organ after the skin.

When we have symptoms like fatigue, acne, skin disorders, waking from sleep between 1am and 3am, moodiness, red eyes, bloating and a general feeling of sluggishness and imbalance, it is often a sign your liver needs a rest and detox. The quickest way to fatigue the liver is by drinking alcohol or coffee; suffer from stress and lack of sleep and by eating foods that are high in fats.

A great naturopath once explained to me how busy the liver actually can be – breaking down food, sorting, sifting and absorbing each day. When we let the liver rest it can regenerate and do any additional jobs it puts aside, and we feel amazing.

THINGS WE CAN DO:

TAKE A BREAK: Do a mini liver cleanse and have a day or two drinking herbal tea, fresh organic fruit juice, and lots of water. If this is too challenging, then have a late lunch once or twice a week and skip dinner.

ST MARY'S THISTLE: This supports stage one and two of the detoxification process. Ensure you take a practitioner grade supplement once a day for a few weeks. St Mary's thistle is great if you are experiencing hormonal problems, acne or have been hitting the wines too hard.

NO DAIRY: Dairy products are so full on for the digestive system, which directly puts pressure and extra work on the liver. Ditch the dairy for a few days and see how much lighter and cleaner you feel.

DANDELION TEA: Dandelion tea is marvellous for maintaining optimum liver, kidney and gallbladder function. It also purifies the blood.

STRETCH AND YOGA POSTURES: Yoga helps eliminate all blockages in the body. The liver meridian runs down the inner thigh and all the way down the inside of your legs. Stretch daily to bring circulation and energy flow to the area.

EASY ON THE JUNGLE JUICE: Alcohol causes inflammation everywhere in the body, especially the stomach, liver and oesophagus. Excessive intake of alcohol damages and congests the liver and can lead to cirrhosis.

DON'T WORRY, BE HAPPY: In Traditional Chinese Medicine it is believed that if you are angry or stressed you create too much heat in the liver. If the liver is not functioning well, the flow of qi is stagnated, resulting in feelings of frustration, depression, irritability, anger, pain, stiffness in the chest, lumps in the throat and abdominal problems. Positive emotions influence the smooth flow of liver qi, and stagnated liver qi affects the emotions adversely. A happy liver allows people to feel composed, content, satisfied and relaxed.

THE MIRACLE MINERAL

"There is no doubt that disease and illness are a result of an unwholesome diet and improper behaviour."

Since I have started taking magnesium I can honestly say my life has changed. I sleep better, I have much more energy, I feel less congested, I have softer hair and stronger nails; I no longer suffer joint pain, back pain or headaches. Everything feels in better working order within my body. Magnesium is one of the most abundant minerals in the human body and is essential for good health. If you suffer from headaches, insomnia and shakiness after exercise, as well as restless legs and mood swings, you may be depleted in this mineral. Magnesium is responsible for more than 300 biochemical reactions in the body and is therefore essential for good health. It regulates blood sugar levels, keeps the heart rhythm steady, the immune system strong, and balances the central nervous system. Magnesium also regenerates body cells and keeps our bones strong. Magnesium is great for assisting with disorders such as hypertension, insomnia and diabetes.

Magnesium can be found in dark green leafy vegetables, nuts and seeds, whole grains, meat and seafood. However, I highly recommend you discuss taking an additional supplement with your health practitioner, as magnesium is greatly depleted in our soil and not getting into our fruit, vegetables and nuts. It is further diminishing in plants because of the use of potassium and phosphorus laden fertilisers. Food processing removes magnesium. High carbohydrate and high fat diets increase the need for magnesium, as does physical and mental stress. Diuretic medications, regular saunas, Bikram or hot yoga and insulin further deplete magnesium levels in the body. It is important that magnesium intake is upped as we age.

How to drink:

1 cup room temperature purified water
½ tsp magnesium chloride
Stir thoroughly and sip

Personally I believe magnesium is best taken at night to ensure relaxed muscles and a good night's sleep. Some experts suggest magnesium is best absorbed during the day along with vitamin C and calcium.

AROMATHERAPY

"Life is measured by the smells we inhale."

The word aromatherapy comes from two words: aroma, meaning fragrance; and therapy, meaning treatment. Aromatherapy is an ancient healing system that dates back to early Egyptian times. It is a science that is based on the use of pure essential oils that are derived from the flowers, leaves, roots, seeds and stems of plants.

Our sense of smell is one of our strongest senses. We respond to smells emotionally more than our other senses. Apart from delivering beautiful aromas that encourage us to feel relaxed and happy, pure essential oils have long been used to treat many physical conditions within the body and stimulate healing. Pure essential oils can influence blood pressure, the digestive system, the nervous system and balance hormone levels. They also have potent antiviral and antibacterial properties.

Aromatherapy is a profound medicinal art based on nature. It affects the whole person—mind, body, and spirit. It is a very powerful and fast growing holistic modality using pure essential oils to treat and cure health problems on both a physical and emotional level. Conventional medicine and its technologies were once the preferred method of treating health conditions. Today, the use of herbs, roots and plants for healing is radically making a comeback!

THERAPY

"Holistic thinking is based on love, empathy and respect."

Natural therapies are unique in the sense that they provide an opportunity to explore, deal with, and heal illness. We can start to understand ourselves better as a whole by addressing physical and emotional issues.

The holistic approach to medicine identifies the whole person—body, mind and spirit—rather than just focusing on a particular physical, mental or emotional state. The wholeness of its scope encourages you to find a lifestyle that is most appropriate for you. The techniques used in holistic medicine are gentle and effective, promoting optimal patient wellbeing and stress reduction.

SOME EXAMPLES OF HOLISTIC THERAPEUTIC MODALITIES ARE:

NATUROPATHY – Naturopaths are the doctors of natural medicine that undergo extensive study of the human body. Naturopathy is based on science and the ancient wisdom of natural medicine, drawing from a comprehensive range of therapies tailored to suit your personal needs.

MASSAGE THERAPY – Massage improves circulation by bringing oxygen to the cells and body tissues. It relieves tension and pain, alleviates physical and mental stress, and greatly increases flexibility and mobility in the body.

REFLEXOLOGY – Certain areas on the feet and hands are linked to the organs and glands. Applying pressure to these reflex areas promotes health in the corresponding organs and glands through energetic pathways called meridians.

CRANIAL SACRAL THERAPY – Cranial sacral therapy is a gentle hands on therapy used to reduce stress, improve sleep, increase energy and enhance organ function. It helps alleviate migraines and headaches, and is used for helping to overcome orthopaedic tribulations and birth trauma.

KINESIOLOGY – Kinesiology is a natural health system that combines muscle testing with the principles of Traditional Chinese Medicine to assess energy and body function. It employs a variety of gentle yet powerful healing techniques to improve health, wellbeing and vitality.

HOMEOPATHY – Homeopathy is a natural form of medicine that uses plant, mineral or animal substances to stimulate the body's ability to heal itself. Homeopathic medicine must be harmonized to the individual on all levels – physical, mental and emotional.

AROMATHERAPY – Aromatherapy is the holistic practice of using pure essential oils extracted from plants and flowers to treat the physical, mental and spiritual body. Pure essential oils stimulate receptors in the nose, which relay messages to the limbic system, the part of the brain that regulates emotions.

OSTEOPATHY – Osteopathy is a manual therapy that recognises the important link between body structure and function. Osteopaths identify how the skeleton, joints, muscles, nerves, circulation, connective tissue and internal organs function as a whole.

COLONICS – Colonic hydrotherapy is a helpful method of removing waste from the colon or large intestine. A colon, cleansed of toxins, is healthier and able to more effectively move food through the digestive system and absorb vital nutrients, proteins, water and minerals back into the bloodstream.

NUTRITIONAL THERAPY – Nutritional therapy is based on the science of nutrition. It uses food as the medicine to balance and restore the body to a state of good health, and to treat and prevent disease.

YOGA – Yoga effectively balances, purifies and strengthens the body, mind and soul. It leads you to perfect health, perfect mind control and inner peace.

MEDITATION – Meditation means awareness. Yoga, surfing, breathing, gardening, cooking or painting may be your method of meditation, providing you with freedom from the fluctuations of the mind. The purpose of meditation is to reach a heightened level of spiritual awareness.

REIKI – Reiki is an emotionally rebalancing and healing experience that assists with healing on an emotional, physical and spiritual level, as well as relaxation. Reiki is used to treat sleep disorders, depression, stress, chronic pain and life trauma.

DANCE THERAPY – Dance is an expressive therapy for helping emotional, cognitive, social, behavioural and physical conditions. Through movement we recognise the interrelationship between the physical, emotional and cognitive dimensions of our behaviour.

ART THERAPY – Art therapy is the creative process of making art as a means to exploring your inner experiences and past traumas. In addition to creating art, the art therapist may use relaxation and visualisation techniques to help you focus, relax and express yourself.

LIFE COACHING – Life coaching begins with an awareness that all people are born with the ability to be, do or have, whatever they want in life. The coach helps the client to identify what they want, and suggests strategies and tactics that will take the client from where they are now to where they want to be.

TRADITIONAL CHINESE MEDICINE – Traditional Chinese Medicine is a holistic medical system that combines the use of acupuncture, herbs, nutrition, massage and tai chi to bring the body into harmony and balance.

ACUPUNCTURE – Acupuncture promotes health and alleviates pain and suffering. Acupuncturists insert needles into specified meridian points in the body to influence, restore and balance the flow of qi, also known as vital energy.

SHIATSU – Shiatsu is a form of massage that stimulates acupressure points to balance the meridians. It incorporates soft and firm massage, verbal consultation, exercises and nutritional advice.

HERBAL MEDICINE – Herbal medicine is one of the oldest forms of health care. It has been practised for centuries to cure a number of illnesses. Herbal medicines can be taken in the form of tablets, extracts, teas, pure essential oils and tinctures.

AYURVEDIC THERAPY – Originating in India, ayurveda is one of the world's oldest medical systems, which emphasises balancing the body through nutrition, lifestyle, exercise and cleansing. Ayurveda teaches that health is maintained by the balancing of three subtle energies known as doshas—vata, pitta and kapha.

If you would like to see a holistic practitioner, make sure you seek out a qualified professional that is a member of a recognised association. These practitioners are becoming more common, and you can find details for them online and in health food stores, clinics, hospitals and natural therapy colleges.

TICK-TOCK

"Great things come from physical and emotional awareness."

The 21st century lifestyle is generating countless illnesses and imbalances in the body. We must learn to slow down, listen to the body and respect our obligation to be healthy. According to the ancient practice of Traditional Chinese Medicine, the body has a series of channels or meridians through which energy flows. This energy affects the internal organs and gives life force to the entire body. Meridians become blocked when the yin and yang balance are disturbed by a hectic 24/7 lifestyle involving stress, poor diet, emotional trauma and lack of rest.

According to Traditional Chinese Medicine the body has a 24 hour cycle that affects our energy (qi) states. Every two hours of the day a different organ and meridian system is energised. By living in sync with the 24 hour cycle we can save our qi by restoring and balancing our health. Our body has a natural balance of yin and yang: yin is cold and yang is hot. Yin and yang must be in balance for optimal health and the concept of living in alignment with our energy cycle is to achieve the best possible equilibrium. If we can do the precise things physically and emotionally at the right time according to the Chinese body clock, we will increase our longevity and happiness. Remember this is an ancient wisdom that has been practiced for thousands of years, keeping people healthy and happy.

THE 24 HOUR QI AND ORGAN CYCLE IS WHEN THE QI AND ENERGY FLOW CONCENTRATES ON A SPECIFIC ORGAN AT A SPECIFIC TIME.

5AM TO 7AM

Relates to the large intestine, which is responsible for our bowel movements. It is not surprising that many people move their bowels first thing in the morning during the TCM-optimal elimination time. It is important to have at least one bowel movement per day, allowing for the removal of toxins. Start the day with a warm glass of purified water and lemon, do a few stretches and relax into the morning. This will help you let go of the past. If you wake during these hours with indigestion then cut from your diet whatever it is you ate the night before.

7AM TO 9AM

Relates to the stomach, making this the perfect time of day to eat your breakfast, as digestive function is optimal. The stomach is said to be the emotional centre of the body, where we tend to hold negative energy, worry and fear. Take advantage of the peak stomach qi time by meditating, breathing out any resistance or anger, then indulge in a healthy and peaceful breakfast.

9AM TO 11AM

Relates to the spleen, which in Traditional Chinese Medicine, is considered to be the most important digestive organ. It helps digest our breakfast; it receives nutrients from the foods and beverages we consume, and turns them into blood. The spleen reflects our thoughts and intentions. Symptoms of low spleen energy are fluid retention, fatigue and unhealthy mouth and lips. Over thinking, over working and mental exertion all cause weakness in spleen energy. Restore this energy by talking about your worries and practising control over destructive thought patterns. Cut back on sweet foods and relax whenever you can.

11AM TO 1PM

Relates to the heart, making this a good time to express your feelings. Avoid overheating and vigorous exercise during the 11am to 1pm period. Instead engage in activities that make you happy, joyful and enthusiastic, like listening to music and spending joyful moments with friends. Dizziness, heart palpitations and insomnia are signs of weak heart energy. To be healthy the heart requires human connection, love and a healthy balanced diet abundant in antioxidant-rich organic vegetables and healthy fats such as olive and flaxseed oil.

1PM TO 3PM

Relates to the small intestine, and like the heart, the related emotion is joy. This small intestine period is a fantastic time to eat lunch, nourishing your body with wholesome easily digestible foods that bring you satisfaction and enjoyment. Avoid carbonated cold drinks at this time, as they disturb digestion.

3PM TO 5PM

Relates to the bladder. The bladder energy can be strengthened by letting go of any fears you may have. Feeling depressed during this time indicates that you need to explore the issues you have involving jealousy and resentment. Physical symptoms such as urinary track infections and lower back pain manifest when the bladder energy is stagnant. Salty foods encourage bladder energy, so having a miso or savoury soup at this time is beneficial.

5PM TO 7PM

Relates to the kidneys. The kidneys are the great reservoir of life force for the entire body. Emotions related to the kidneys are directly linked to willpower, and include feelings of safety, aloofness and loneliness. Kidney energy is linked to our parents. When kidney energy is low we will feel lonely, have low libido, lack strength and courage. During the hours of 5pm to 7pm, switch off from the day, acknowledge your skills and strengths, have sex and laugh. Some kidney strengthening foods are lamb, kidney beans, seaweed, walnuts, pumpkin and plums.

7PM TO 9PM

Relates to the pericardium. The pericardium is closely linked to the heart and is associated with feelings of love and happiness. Physical changes and alteration in your wellbeing between 7pm and 9pm may therefore reflect your level of joy. Keep your pericardium healthy by engaging in acts of creativity and self expression. This is a perfect time to have loving sex with somebody you deeply love.

9PM TO IIPM

Relates to the triple burner. There is no corresponding organ to the triple burner. It metabolizes all the bodily fluids including blood, sweat, tears, saliva and urine, and it is responsible for the production, transportation and removal of foods and fluids within the body. During this time digestion, elimination and nourishment of the immune system are taking place, making the hours between 9pm and 11pm the optimum time for sleep, relaxation and engaging in activities you enjoy.

IIPM TO IAM

Relates to the gallbladder, which is associated with courage and the use of wise judgment. Problems with making rash decisions, nervousness and timidity during these hours reflect a gallbladder imbalance. If you have dreams where you feel angry and frustrated, it is also an indication your gallbladder energy is out of balance. Fatty foods and hydrogenated oils damage the gallbladder. Regularly eat fresh green vegetables and olive, flaxseed and fish oils to ensure stagnant bile and cholesterol are cleared, keeping the gallbladder happy and healthy.

1AM TO 3AM

Relates to the liver. The liver detoxifies the body physically and emotionally. The feelings linked most strongly to the liver are anger, frustration, bitterness and resentment. It's a good idea to be asleep during these liver hours to allow maximum energy to be diverted for detoxification; this explains why an early night's sleep is harmonizing for a healthy body and mind. If you often wake up during the hours of 1am to 3am it may very well indicate your liver needs some cleansing. If you throw up during these hours you must eliminate alcohol for at least three months. Green leafy vegetables and dandelion herbal tea support liver health.

3AM TO 5AM

Relates to the lungs. Wisdom is said to be derived from the lungs and the emotions that directly speak to them are grief and sadness. If you find yourself waking up during these hours it is a key indication that you need to explore your emotional life. Deal with your emotions by talking to a friend or counsellor; journal writing and meditation will also help. On a physical level, eating apples, practicing yoga and learning to breathe correctly support lung health. Sleep with your windows open to ensure you get enough fresh air, and vaporise pure eucalyptus, lemon and lavender essential oils in your bedroom to clear and calm your entire respiratory system.

WHAT'S YOUR TYPE?

"Give, give, give: it is the secret to your abundance."

Have you ever noticed that some people can eat whatever they want without problems, while others suffer from skin conditions, allergies, bloating, indigestion and fatigue? And why can some people eat masses of food and not put on weight, whilst others eat very little but put on weight easily? The blood type diet is all about your genetic inheritance and the reaction that occurs between your blood and the foods you eat. The blood type diet is just another beautiful reason why, as a biochemical individual we are all so uniquely different. Everybody has a particular blood type that is inherited from our parents. You can find out your blood type by asking your parents, donating blood or by requesting a blood test from a doctor.

BLOOD TYPE O

Blood type O, the oldest blood type in the world, evolved around 40,000 BC; people with this blood type have the hardiest digestive systems. Traditionally they are the meat eaters and require animal protein, seafood, as well as fruit and vegetables for good health. They should minimise their intake of carbohydrates, wheat, dairy, gluten products, and avoid drinking coffee. Dandelion tea and green tea are perfect alternatives. People with blood type O tend to have an underactive thyroid and sluggish metabolisms. They should give their body plenty of sea vegetables and seafood to obtain natural iodine to stimulate the thyroid gland and avoid weight gain. The best exercises for type Os are energetic workouts like jogging, power walking and aerobics.

BLOOD TYPE A

People with blood type A evolved from the hunter meat eaters to the farmers and grain gatherers. They have fragile digestive systems and cannot digest animal protein easily. They are recognised as the classic vegetarians of the human species. Type As benefit from a diet of whole grains, legumes, fruits and vegetables, and tofu, and should avoid animal protein and dairy products. Type As tend to experience difficulty absorbing vitamin B12 from the foods they eat. Vitamin B12 is normally found in red meat, however it is also found in vegetable protein foods such as spirulina and soy products. The inability to absorb vitamin B12 sufficiently from food tends to make the person with blood type A prone to anaemia. Therefore, enhancing the diet with a vitamin B12 supplement is critical. Spirulina is ideal, because it is a whole food that is very high in vitamin B12. The best exercises for type As are those that are calming like yoga, tai chi, and walking.

BLOOD TYPE B

This blood type developed between 15,000 and 10,000 BC. People with blood type B have tolerant digestive systems, and can eat most foods without difficulty. Foods type Bs should avoid include corn, buckwheat, lentils, peanuts, and sesame seeds, as they may encourage weight gain. Just like type Os, type Bs are inclined to have difficulty with gluten and wheat products, which can result sudden drops in their blood sugar levels. Type B people can tolerate dairy products more than the other blood types.

BLOOD TYPE AB

Blood type AB is the rarest blood type. It has only been around for about 1000 years and less than five per cent of the world's population have it. You combine the best and the worst of both blood types A and B to determine what is best for the AB type. Foods that are bad for those that are type A or type B are generally also bad for those that are type AB. Like type A, type ABs do not produce enough stomach acid to effectively digest large quantities of animal protein such as red meat and poultry, yet they do benefit from some animal protein such as lamb, rabbit and turkey. Type ABs should eat pineapples to aid the digestion of animal protein foods.

WHEAT FREE LIFE

"Do things from the heart, rather than the ego."

Many people suffer from irritable bowel syndrome (IBS), constipation, abdominal discomfort, bloating, weight gain, gas, skin conditions, lethargy, body congestion, joint pain and sinusitis. These symptoms are generally related to an allergy or intolerance involving wheat and gluten foods. In 2009 a naturopath diagnosed me with having the coeliac gene. I understood that this means a family member in my bloodline had coeliac disease and ignored the condition, resulting in an intolerance to gluten. When I speak with my clients about their wheat intolerance symptoms, I strongly advise they exclude wheat and gluten from their diet for a few weeks to see if this is the underlying cause of the problem. These people generally look at me like I am a crazy person, responding with, "What do you mean, give up bread, pasta and tomato sauce?"

I have noticed that some people prefer to put up with discomfort and suffer, than give up the foods they like and are used to. I, however, choose to live life to my full potential, feeling clean, energetic and pain free. Any elimination diet should be carried out with the support of a doctor or naturopath, ensuring you don't deprive yourself of vital nutrients. Below are some gluten-free alternatives that are delicious so you won't feel like you're missing out.

Use white and brown rice flakes for porridge. Eat more Asian style cuisine by opting for rice and rice noodles instead of bread and pasta at meal times. Purchase bread and pasta made from buckwheat, millet and spelt flours. Suss out your local market for all the gluten-free alternatives to breads, pasta, cereal, muffins, muesli bars, soy sauce and anything else you normally eat. Many cafés will offer gluten-free bread these days , and many restaurants will have something gluten-free on the menu too. Save on cash and eliminate gluten by making your very own bread, sauces, cakes, muffins and pasta with any of the following gluten-free flours.

ALMOND FLOUR – Almond flour and meal are both simply ground up almonds. Used alone or in combination with other flours, almond meal is used in breads, cakes and pastries. I really like the moistness it brings to cakes and muffins.

CHICKPEA FLOUR – There are two types of chickpea flours: unroasted, which is sandy yellow in colour and almost nut-like in flavour, and roasted. Chickpea flour is often used in Indian cooking to make fritters, desserts and savoury balls. Throughout the Middle East it is used to make falafel.

BROWN RICE FLOUR – This is milled from unpolished brown rice and contains bran, which gives it a high fibre content. Brown rice flour is ideal for making potato gnocchi. Its wholemeal flavour and texture gives the gnocchi an earthy flavour.

BUCKWHEAT FLOUR – This is not a form of wheat, but is actually related to rhubarb. It has a strong nutty taste and is perfect for savoury pastry, pasta, muffins and banana bread. Blend with rice flour or cornflour to reduce the nuttiness.

POTATO STARCH/FLOUR – This fine white flour made from potatoes has a light potato flavour which is virtually undetectable in the finished dish. Potato flour is ideal in sponge cakes and biscuits, and it can be added as a thickener to casseroles, soups and stews.

QUINOA FLOUR – Quinoa flour is produced from quinoa, a grain native to South America. It is a somewhat unique grain, in that it has a very high protein content which made it a critical part of the Andean diet for centuries. This wonderful grain bakes beautifully in cakes and pastries. Puffed quinoa is a great alternative to couscous or oats.

RICE FLOUR – Available in supermarkets, white rice flour is finer than brown rice flour and has a more delicate texture when cooked. It is great for making noodles, pastry, sponge cakes and bread.

SOYA FLOUR – Soya flour is high protein nutrient-rich flour with a nice nutty taste. When combined with other flours it is a very successful alternative to conventional flour. It is not normally used on its own. Soya flour also has a high fat content, and is good blended with other flours and water to make egg-free pastries and cakes.

ARROWROOT FLOUR – Ground from the root of the arrowroot plant this flour is a great thickening agent, making it ideal for sauces. It's tasteless, and the fine powder becomes clear when cooked.

TAPIOCA FLOUR – Made from the root of the cassava plant, tapioca flour adds a kind of chewiness to baking and is also a good thickener. It is perfect for casseroles and for binding rissole and hamburger patties.

DID THE CHICKEN EVER GET TO CROSS THE ROAD?

"Learn from yesterday, live for today, hope for tomorrow. The important thing is not to stop questioning."

Nine times out of 10 the chicken on your plate, never got the chance to even walk, let alone cross the road. Conventional or battery farmed chickens sit in a small cage pretty much the whole 40 days of their sad lives. They are pumped with hormones and have little opportunity to move around as this makes them fatter quicker. The chickens are given a feed that is full of antibiotics, containing traces of chemicals, pesticides, herbicides, artificial fertilisers and genetically modified waste. If you choose to eat the meat and eggs of a battery farmed chicken, you too are ingesting these poisons, and supporting a cruel and unacceptable practice of farming.

Certified free-range chickens are free to roam outside during the day and forage amongst natural vegetation. Free-range chickens have lower stocking densities than conventional chickens, and are fed a healthy diet free from growth hormones and antibiotics. Certified organic poultry is fed certified organic food, some of which the farmer is supposed to produce himself. The chickens are not medicated in any way, and have a similar quality of life to that of free-range chickens.

Many people prefer to eat free-range and organic poultry because it gives them confidence that it does not contain the antibiotics and steroids that are used to treat conventional chickens. Free-range and organically farmed chickens live longer, taste much better and are safer to eat.

WHY FAST?

"Throughout history, people have fasted for religious and political reasons; others regularly fast because it instinctively feels good for them."

It is beneficial to regularly fast as this gives the metabolic organs a much needed rest. Fasting is one of the most natural and inexpensive ways to heal, cleanse and rejuvenate the entire body. Be mindful that fasting is not for everyone; it is dependent on age, medical history and living conditions. I'm all about the regular fast, finding it to be a wondrous journey of self-discovery, self-discipline and self-control. Be mindful that you have to be in the right head space to fast – make up your mind, and just do it. I try to fast two to three times per year. Below are a few fasting programs you can do regularly, even for just one to two days.

JUICE FASTING – Juice fasting involves drinking the juice of different seasonal fruits and vegetables that are specifically detoxing, astringent and purifying every two to three hours. Choose mainly organic green vegetables to juice as they are highly alkaline and cleansing. Some people follow a juice fasting program for up to a week.

WATER FASTING – Water fasting involves drinking purified room temperature water all day just for one day. Adding fresh lemon juice is recommended for extra cleansing.

MINIMAL AND ELIMINATION EATING – Let's be honest, most of us stuff our faces! Having the courage to give your body a break from toxins is a very good choice; do this by eating small meals every two hours consisting of only fruit and vegetables. Totally eliminate proteins, fats, sugar, stimulants, dairy and meat. This fast can be done for as long as you need.

HERBAL DETOX – This detox is all about sipping on good quality herbal teas all day, generally something detoxifying like red clover, nettle, liquorice and dandelion. Drinking water with a herbal tea fast will aid the cleansing process.

BROWN RICE DETOX – Cook up a big batch of organic brown rice; eat this, and only this, at all your meal times for a few days. You may add tamari soy sauce to the rice if you wish. At the end of the following day the visit to the bathroom will be a long one.

SOUP FAST – Eat organic vegetable soup all day. The combination of nutrients and warm liquid will gently move through your system hydrating and cleansing the organs. Soup is very easily digested and highly nutritious.

KICHARI STEW – This is a popular food consumed during any cleansing period, involving a simple cooked recipe of basmati rice, lentils, water, turmeric, ginger, lemon, salt and pepper. In fact, a kichari fast is preferred in many Ayurvedic treatments over raw, juice or water fasts. Aside from being nutritious, it tastes really good too.

Everybody is so beautifully different. If you are feeling you need a good clean out or you simply want to give your digestive system a break, speak to a professional about the fast that will be most beneficial and appropriate for you. I always encourage my customers to take Epsom salt baths, meditate, get a massage, rest and drink lots of water and herbal teas when doing any fast. A fast can be challenging and often confronting, leaving you feeling cranky and depressed. Once you begin to push through these normal emotions you will find that you are rewarded with a clear body and mind.

WINO

"The French say that you should describe wine, just as you would describe your best friends."

Wine is beautiful, a welcome guest in homes all over the world. Used in moderation, wine, particularly the red varieties, is said to lower cholesterol and fight heart disease. If this is true, my cousins Daniel and Paul must have the healthiest hearts and cholesterol levels in Australia! As the quality of Australian organic wine continues to improve, organic wine drinking is becoming a popular pastime for many Australians, or should I say a healthy obsession...

Certified organic wine is made from grapes that are grown organically, prohibiting the use of pesticides, herbicides, fungicides, chemical fertilisers and synthetic chemicals. Many people prefer to buy organic wine because they want to help to reduce their carbon footprint, appreciate the flavour of organically produced wine and are interested in the health benefits of organic produce. I am personally motivated to seek out organic wine because of the simple fact that it doesn't give me a hangover. If anyone has ever experienced a true wine hangover you will try drinking organic and you will understand what I mean.

Organic winemakers employ organic farming methods to obtain the strongest and richest grapes possible. These methods have minimal impact on the environment, and the resulting wines reflect the farmers' dedication to quality. Organic wine allows some sprays to be used that are not harmful, and the wine that is produced contains the absolute minimum preservatives required to protect the wine quality. Like buying organic food and skincare products, please look for an organic stamp of certification on the bottle – without this symbol the product may not be legitimate.

A LITTLE RAY OF SUNSHINE

"Happiness is a morning spent in the sunshine. Take delight in the simple pleasures of life; when only the fanciest of materialistic devices make you happy, you will always be discontent."

The best source of vitamin D is UV-B radiation from the sun. Vitamin D is necessary for absorption and utilisation of minerals like calcium, and we need adequate amounts of vitamin D for healthy bones. Vitamin D is also found in oily fish like tuna and salmon, and in eggs, as well as in fortified foods like milk and breakfast cereals.

A friend of mine who has worked in pre-schools for many years gave me the low down on how strict the system is about sun smart practice. This policy is taken very seriously, enforcing many rules, including times and days of the year that children are allowed to play outside, and that everyday staff and children must wear broad brimmed hats, protective clothing and 30+ broad spectrum waterproof sunscreen. My friend also informed me that in all her years of teaching, she has never encountered so many sick children, constantly battling all types of nasty colds, flus, allergies and skin conditions. You see vitamin D is a major stimulator of the immune system and without it we get sick. I am very aware that there are more people in Australia treated for skin cancer than anywhere else in the world, but I do believe moderate sunshine is healthy. I guess what I am trying to say is think about balance, get a little sun, just 10 minutes a day is sufficient to get enough vitamin D to keep you happy and healthy. Always choose organic and zinc based sunscreen that is free from synthetic and toxic ingredients. Coconut, jojoba and avocado plant oils provide natural sun protection.

DELICIOUS TREATS

"All earthly delights are to be enjoyed."

When cravings emerge for something deliciously sweet, salty, oily or hearty there is only one thing to do... surrender to it! Keep your indulgences healthy and nourishing and eat something amazing, being mindful not to eat foods that are toxic to your body in your clouded state of craving. Below are some ideas for healthy pig-outs that are 100 per cent natural and still phenomenally delicious. These healthy and nutritious treats will completely satisfy your cravings leaving you feeling far from deprived.

FRESH DATES WITH PEANUT BUTTER – Buy the plumpest freshest dates you can get, slice in half and remove the seed. Spoon some cold crunchy peanut butter into the centre; place the date firmly back together; eat and enjoy the mouth orgasm! Almond or cashew butter can be used with the date combo if peanuts are not your scene. You can do the same by spooning a teaspoon of almond butter, or tahini onto a juicy dried fig.

REAL CHOCOLATE – Hit up the health food store for a block of good quality organic chocolate, because nothing beats it. Be sure to carefully read the list of ingredients to ensure it is free from refined sugar, wheat and dairy. You will find the alternatives to these ingredients are things like cane sugar, stevia, goji berries, rice syrup, dates, cashew butter and cocoa butter. If you feel the need, you have permission to eat the whole block!

CHUNKY SWEET POTATOES CHIP WITH AIOLI – Skin and chop up a sweet potato into wedge style pieces, lay the wedges in an oven tray and sprinkle with olive oil, salt, pepper and paprika. Bake for 30 minutes, or until crispy and golden. Whip up home-made aioli by placing one cup of olive oil, one egg, one garlic clove, one tablespoon of lemon juice, a few mustard seeds, a sprinkle of sea salt and two peppercorns into a food processor and blend for two minutes.

PINEAPPLE AND BANANA FRITTERS – Try dipping a few pineapple and banana pieces into a bowl of whisked egg, then coat them in rice flour and some gluten-free bread crumbs. Refrigerate for one hour before gently frying them in coconut oil until they are perfectly golden. Serve with natural soy ice cream, a sprinkle of ground ginger and grated coconut.

BERRIES FONDUE – Get your hands on some organic raspberries, blueberries and strawberries. Wash and prepare the berries in a fancy dessert glass. In a bowl, combine two tablespoons of organic cocoa powder, two tablespoons of coconut cream and a teaspoon of raw honey. Mix until it's perfectly smooth and then drizzle onto the awaiting berry mix, and garnish with shaved dark chocolate and coconut.

Organic apples and spicy cream – Peel, slice and steam two organic apples for about 10 minutes until tender. In a small bowl combine a little cinnamon, nutmeg, honey and a dash of boiling water, and mix into a runny kind of sauce. Pour the sauce over your steamy apples and finish with a tablespoon of sheep's milk yoghurt and a few raisins or sultanas. Hot, spicy and delicious!

Home-made hamburgers – Let loose and cook up some 100 per cent natural beef or vegetable patties. Serve the patty on a fresh buttered spelt or sourdough bun along with a fried egg, sliced lettuce, mashed avocado, caramelised onion, tomato, goat cheese and home-made relish. Garnish with coriander, cracked pepper and sea salt. Hearty and healthy!

Home-made raw ice cream – If you feel adventurous, make some of your very own signature ice cream. There are plenty of recipes and raw food websites out there to guide you. Some healthy ingredients to use in place of milk, cream and sugar are coconut cream, soy and raw goat's milk, coconut flesh, avocado, banana, tofu, agave syrup, honey, nuts, fresh mint and cocoa nibs.

Google some goodness – Be a true *Hippy in the City* and google natural recipes for healthier alternatives to your favourite food cravings. My top suggestions are organic buckwheat pancakes, vegan brownies, vegan coconut ice cream, choc chip spelt cookies and gluten-free sticky date pudding. If you come across any recipes that use refined sugar, just modify them by using palm sugar or honey.

Takeaway – The best takeaway options are those establishments that use natural and traditional methods of cooking. If you are going to indulge in some takeaway, choose a healthier option like Thai, Japanese, Vietnamese, Korean, Indonesian, Lebanese, Greek, Nepalese, Mexican or South American cuisine. It is appropriate to ask the chef to make your meal gluten and sugar free and not to use MSG.

CHAPTER TWO

TIPS AND TRICKS

"It's important for me to share with you almost every tip and trick I know. Of course all advice, tips and tricks offer a natural solution. The practice of holistic medicine has been used since the beginning of time, throughout every culture and civilisation all over the world. The healing benefits that nature promises are true, and are always so multifunctional and versatile. Often a plant that is good for sleep is great for healing sores, or perhaps a certain essential oil that helps with depression can also be used to treat skin fungus."

"Nature supplies a remedy for everything and everyone."

INDIGESTION

Brew fresh or dried herbs of fennel, peppermint, lemon balm, chamomile and make into a tea. Apple cider vinegar shots and sipping on fresh lemon and warm water will also help balance pH levels. Doing some yoga stretches, focusing on side stretching and deep breathing will assist digestion and discomfort.

COLD SORES

Cold sores are caused by the herpes simplex virus. There are two variants, HSV-1 and HSV-2. The first usually causes oral outbreaks around the lips and mouth. As soon as you feel the tingle, apply a frozen ice cube to the area for 20 minutes. Quickly follow by applying neat bergamot, patchouli, lavender or tea tree essential oil to the blister. Having a lysine-rich diet and taking lysine supplements can heal and reduce symptoms of cold sores. Immunity boosting and lysine-rich foods are red meat, beans, eggs, figs, broccoli, seaweed, ginger and garlic. Vitamin C and zinc supplements are best for healing cold sores quickly and efficiently. Eliminate arginine-rich foods such as chocolate and nuts that can make the problem worse.

FAUX TAN REMOVER

In a large glass bowl mix up two cups of coarse salt, one cup of olive oil and the juice of two fresh lemons. Dampen your skin and scrub your entire body for at least 15 minutes, focusing on the knees, hands, feet and elbows. Have a shower and immediately apply a good quality body oil. Repeat the next day if required.

SORE TEETH AND GUMS

Like most health issues, poor dental health is a result of poor diet. Eliminate refined sugary carbohydrates and alcohol and save your teeth. Treat your mouth with warm salt water rinses three times a day and apply 100 per cent clove essential oil to the area that is sore. As clove oil is naturally antibacterial and analgesic it will totally numb the area.

GALLBLADDER AND LIVER PROBLEMS

Take a therapeutic grade of dandelion herbal extract, and drink dandelion herbal tea. Dandelion root is considered a fine liver tonic, promoting healthy gallbladder, pancreas and spleen function. It affects all forms of secretion and excretion from the body. It is an effective cleansing agent with a specific affinity for the liver that will modify and increase its secretions.

ACNE ADVICE

Completely eliminate refined sugar, dairy and wheat for one week and see if you notice a difference to your skin. Most skin conditions are the result of poor digestive health, so people must begin with a gut spring clean. Speak to a health professional about taking a St Mary's thistle, vitex, zinc, vitamin B6 or hormonal balancing supplement to assist with the underlying causes of the acne. Additional things you should do are: drink two litres of purified water per day; eliminate all synthetic skincare products; avoid using hot water on your skin; eat more high alkaline foods; eat more carrots for their skin healing and repairing properties; experiment with blood and liver-cleansing foods such as spinach, kale, kelp, coriander, turmeric, and artichoke; and take dandelion, nettle, and liquorice herbs.

SLUGGISHNESS

If you have pigged out the night before and awake feeling sluggish, squeeze some fresh lemon juice into a glass and a quarter of a teaspoon of cayenne pepper, add a little cold water and top up with half a cup of boiling water. Stir and sip. With a light breakfast, have a vitamin B supplement to restore energy levels. You will soon start to feel fresher and more energised. Spend the rest of the day drinking lots of water, dandelion teas, apple cider vinegar shots and eating light liver-cleansing foods like organic fruits and vegetables.

THE OFFICE

If the wind is Mother Nature's breath, then plants would be her lungs. If you work in an office keep a small plant on your desk, this will help to purify toxins and supply fresher air to your surroundings. Eat your lunch outside when possible to ensure you get 10 minutes a day of sunshine for vital vitamin D. Those who work in an air-conditioned environment must ensure they drink two litres of purified water per day to prevent dehydration and mental fatigue.

TRADITION OF SESAME OIL PULLING

First thing in the morning, before brushing your teeth, eating or drinking, put one tablespoon of sesame oil into your mouth, tilt your chin back and slowly swish, suck, gargle and pull through the teeth. The oil pulls all mucous, bacteria and toxins from your body through your saliva and tongue meridians. According to Ayurvedic medicine, mucous is a poison that must be removed from the body.

STAINED TEETH

Coffee, tea, ciggies, red wine and too many curries all contribute to stained pearlies. Brush your teeth immediately after consuming any of the above. Once in a while brush your teeth using bicarbonate of soda, salt and fresh lemon. It will make your teeth whiter, but if done too often it will strip your teeth of the natural enamel.

WEEKEND SKINNY

If you wish to ditch a few kilos pre-summer or before special event, eliminate all refined sugars, processed foods and simple carbohydrates for one week. Replace salt on food with fresh lemon; drink green kombucha, oolong or lemongrass tea half an hour after meals; and only eat fresh fruits and vegetables before noon as this allows the system to detoxify. Eat very small high protein meals frequently throughout the day, to maintain metabolic function. Your last daily meal should be before 8pm. Relax and sleep well, because when we stress out blockages occur within the emotional centre – the solar plexus, and stomach meridian - resulting in bloating and poor digestion.

LACTATING MOTHERS

Sipping on fennel and fenugreek herbal tea assists in promoting lactation. Increase your intake of green leafy vegetables and make sure you are getting adequate amounts of protein, essential fatty acids, and fibre in your daily diet. Dehydration can cause a reduction in milk supply, so drink plenty of water and other fluids to remain hydrated. Massaging the breasts is also beneficial to clear the milk ducts and improve the flow of your breast milk. Avoid wearing a tight-fitting bra, as this can lead to congested milk ducts.

ULCERATIVE COLITIS

Because ulcerative colitis is a disease that causes inflammation, sores and ulcers in the lining of the rectum and colon, it is important to eat mainly alkaline and anti-inflammatory foods of fresh organic vegetables, cold pressed plant oils and super foods. Treat ulcerative colitis by taking a daily practitioner grade supplement of L-Glutamine, probiotics, coconut oil, turmeric, pure aloe vera juice, magnesium and chlorophyll.

BURNS

Immediately place the affected area under cold running water for at least 10 minutes, then immediately pour five to 10 drops of 100 per cent pure lavender essential oil onto the burn. Repeat the cold water and lavender oil combination every 10 minutes for the next hour. Manuka honey and calendula cream is best applied for the next 48 hours to ensure the wound heals efficiently.

BAD BREATH

Chewing on fresh herbs of fennel, parsley and peppermint will lend a hand in making you kissable again. Eliminating refined sugars and simple carbohydrates also helps, as these foods feed candida, the main cause of poor digestion. A liver cleanse and probiotic supplement can also help to cure bad breath. Using a natural toothpaste that is free from sulphates and incorporates antibacterial essential oils will further assist to keep teeth and gums healthy.

PANDA EYES

Dark circles around the eyes are a common concern that can be caused by a range of bodily issues such as hay fever, dehydration, smoking, iron deficiency, anaemia, lack of sleep and poor functioning of the liver and kidneys. As the physical body is a reflection of its internal status, addressing the possible causes for dark circles is a good place to start. To reduce the appearance of puffiness and dark circles, place cold green tea bags across the eyes and use a soothing eye gel of rose water, aloe vera and chamomile. Start the day with a warm glass of water and fresh lemon to kick start the liver and kidneys, ensuring you look fresh.

HIGH BLOOD PRESSURE

This is a serious health condition that can be caused by a range of factors, including a diet high in saturated fats and low in wholefoods, smoking, alcohol, a lack of exercise and stress. Abnormal blood pressure levels can be balanced with a healthy diet, regular exercise, aromatherapy and yoga. Foods that play a role in actively reducing blood pressure are fruits and vegetables high in potassium, such as garlic, black, navy and kidney beans, sunflower seeds, oats, millet, lentils, salmon, tuna and olive oil. Sipping on green, lemon balm, hibiscus, hawthorn berry and ginseng tea will assist to lower blood pressure.

CELLULITE

Cellulite is the result of too many toxins in the blood. It's a bummer that it affects more women than men. Drink two litres of water per day, break out a daily sweat through exercise or sauna and dry skin brush using upward stroke motions. Make up a weekly cellulite exfoliation scrub of ground organic coffee, sea salt, jojoba, grapefruit, juniper berry and lemon essential oils and then firmly rub into your butt, thighs, calves, stomach and arms. It works a treat, especially before a little black dress occasion. Epsom salt baths, a detox program and regular massages also help keep cellulite at bay.

PUFFY, RED, ITCHY EYES

Puffy, red, itchy eyes can be the result of lack of sleep, stress, allergy, liver congestion, pharmaceutical drugs, wheat intolerance or an MSG food reaction. For puffiness, soak two organic green tea bags in a small bowl of purified water or rose water. Place in the freezer for five minutes, remove and place one tea bag across each eye for 10 minutes. For redness and itchiness soak two cotton pads in a cup of brewed lukewarm organic chamomile tea and sweep over the eye lids up to six times per day. Apply 100 per cent organic jojoba oil over and around the eyes morning and night to hydrate and soothe the irritation. Goji berries have long been used to support human eye health too.

DRY LIPS

Wind, kissing, malnutrition, zinc deficiency and sunburn are all causes of skanky lips! Mix up a little raw sugar and honey and massage for a few moments using a soft toothbrush. Wipe off any excess and coat your lips with a 100 per cent shea and cocoa butter lip balm. Repeat the process three times a day and things should be smooth and well sorted.

ALUMINIUM FREE

Men and women should always use a deodorant that is free from aluminium. Deodorants are applied directly to the skin and are also breathed into the lungs providing two potential paths of aluminium absorption into the body. Aluminium is toxic and has been linked to breast and lymph node cancer. Use a deodorant that states it is aluminium free. Bicarbonate of soda can be used as a natural deodorant – put some in a container and apply on clean, dry skin.

CRACKED LIP CORNERS

Cracked lips are normally a sign of zinc and mineral deficiency. Speak to a health practitioner about taking a liquid zinc supplement. Increase your intake of raw fruits and vegetables, apply a drop of lavender or lime essential oil diluted in some shea butter to the corners of your lips, as these oils greatly lend a hand with healing infection.

Freckles be gone
Although freckles are beautiful, making a face look pretty and unique, they are often a consequence of more than just the sun. Excessive freckles could very well be a sign that you need to look into doing a good gut cleanse or have colonic irrigation. Eating more fresh herbs and applying a blend of jojoba oil and 100 per cent pure oregano essential oil to the skin may help fade out freckles.

Sunspots, uneven skin, and pigmentation
Lack of exfoliation, severe magnesium deficiency, hormonal imbalance, skin fungus and excessive sun exposure can all very well result in imperfect skin. Weekly exfoliation helps to stimulate the production of new skin cells. Products containing fruit enzymes like papaya, lemon and pineapple are wicked for dissolving dead skin cell build up. Consistently using oil containing rosehip, carrot, wheatgerm, sesame, avocado, calendula and jojoba oils will dramatically promote skin regeneration. Speak to a health professional about taking magnesium, fish oil, vitamin C, E and A supplements.

Toe nail fall off disease
As humans, our bodies produce a glue that sticks our finger and toe nails to our skin. When bacteria and water get under the nail, a fungal infection can occur, compromising the nails. Soaking the infected area in patchouli, tea tree, bergamot and lavender pure essential oils, and regularly applying these oils in a jojoba oil base to the area, will kill off the fungal infection. Increasing antifungal and antibiotic food in your diet such as garlic, ginger and chilli also helps the body to fight infection and bacteria.

Fluid retention
How much salt are you having? We all require good salts to aid the absorption of minerals, but processed salt or too much of any salt results in fluid retention. Exercise and massage both greatly help reduce the retention of fluids. Upping your intake of asparagus, astringent and bitter foods is also beneficial. Bathing in Epsom salts and using massage oils that contain fennel, grapefruit, juniper berry and lemon pure essential oils are great for promoting lymphatic drainage.

Haemorrhoids
These inconvenient little growths are unattractive and somewhat uncomfortable, and are often the result of a poor diet that is low in fibre causing constipation. Haemorrhoids are best treated by using a cold witch hazel compress, then applying cypress essential oil diluted in pure coconut oil twice a day.

Irritable bowel pain
Eliminate all the foods that cause inflammation in the gut and digestive system. This includes all products containing wheat, dried fruit, preserved and processed food. Take a daily probiotic, drink two litres of water, have apple cider vinegar in warm water before meals, chew your food slowly, massage your stomach using a diluted blend of fennel, peppermint and lavender essential oils, and investigate the solar plexus chakra to see if you have an energetic blockage there.

Depression and sadness

A handful of cashews equals a Prozac! Cashews are nature's antidepressant. Maca powder, damiana tea, vitamin B supplements, St John's wort and raw cocoa are all natural ways to get you festive again! Talking about your problems, journaling meditation, art therapy and exercise are all helpful tools, too. Clean up your diet, by eliminating all refined sugar and eating only wholesome natural foods. Generally, half the problem of depression and sadness is caused by poor diet.

Alopecia and hair loss

Start by eliminating all synthetic hair products that contain sodium laureth sulphate. Using a shampoo, conditioner and oil treatments that include 100 per cent natural ingredients including rosemary, ginger, cedar wood and geranium pure essential oils will help. Stress, mineral and hormonal imbalance, diet and poor mineral absorption are the main causes for this condition. A regular scalp massage with rosemary and almond oil will help stimulate the scalp and hair growth.

Drinking when eating

Try to avoid drinking when eating because liquids dilute the body's digestive enzymes which you need to break down your food properly. Wait half an hour before and after meals before drinking any fluids. Many ancient religious readings advise to not drink whilst eating.

Gas and bloating

This is often an embarrassing symptom of sluggish digestion, eating too fast, and candida. Always chew your food slowly and mindfully; chew each mouthful 20 times before swallowing. Avoid refined carbohydrate sugary foods and excessive amounts of dried fruit and nuts. Drink fennel, aniseed and peppermint tea. Take two to three charcoal tablets twice per day until the symptoms are alleviated.

Diabetes type 2 – non-insulin dependent

Lowering your blood sugar level is the most important action to take in order to avoid the onset of diabetes, so eliminate all refined carbohydrates and sugar. Consistent intake of magnesium-rich foods can significantly lower your risk of developing diabetes; eat seafood, brown rice, green vegetables, activated almonds, black beans and avocados. Anti-inflammatory foods like flaxseed, whole grains, turmeric and olive oil are beneficial.

Heart health

The heart, also known as the centre of love and happiness, requires a few things to keep it healthy. Cholesterol and blood pressure levels must be balanced; this will be consistent if you have a lifestyle that includes a diet of natural wholefoods, daily exercise and meditation. If heart disease is hereditary in your family, invest in eating more heart protecting foods like olive oil, oatmeal, salmon, dark chocolate and hawthorn berries. Taking a supplement of coenzyme Q10 also assists the proper functioning of the heart.

Clean close shave

To avoid red, lumpy rashes and pimples, it is necessary to exfoliate before you shave, because exfoliation removes dead skin cells before they build up in your razor and attract bacteria, which cause those red pimply rashes. Shaving in a steam room offers a superior shave as the skin's pores are open, and this is lubricating, allowing for a closer cut.

Home-made lube

Use organic coconut or jojoba oil for love making. Both these oils are wonderful for the skin and our glands, they are similar to the oils our bodies produce. Do not use an oil of any kind if you are using a condom during intercourse.

Healthy hair

Luscious healthy hair requires protein to rebuild and strengthen it. Before you wash your hair apply 100 per cent pure almond oil to the scalp and massage it through to the ends. Almond oil provides the hair and skin with protein and nutrients for growth and repair. Leave the oil in overnight or at least for a few hours before thoroughly shampooing. Rosemary and chamomile pure essential oils are both good for the hair. Foods that top the list for healthy hair and its growth are wild salmon, green leafy vegetables, bananas, eggs, nuts and legumes.

Scabies

Scabies mites can drive a person insane! It's important to treat the condition quickly and efficiently. Clove bud pure essential oil has anti-microbial compounds that can help treat scabies. Blend 30 drops of pure clove bud essential oil into 100ml of jojoba oil, shake well and apply the entire mixture evenly over the whole body. Allow it to penetrate into the skin for at least 20 minutes. For further relief have a warm bath in apple cider vinegar and lavender essential oil. Repeat the treatment for three consecutive days.

Insomnia

Eliminate all refined sugar, coffee and stimulants from your diet. Speak to a health professional about taking a magnesium supplement and the herbs of valerian, chamomile and passion flower. Burn a blend of orange, chamomile, lavender and neroli essential oils in the evening to help you relax. Kinesiology, acupuncture and cranial sacral therapy may help with the underlying causes of insomnia. Regular exercise, practising of yoga, and meditation is also beneficial.

Moodiness

First ask yourself, what are the hidden meanings behind my feelings? Avoid refined sugar, which will make your blood sugar unstable and lead to a later crash, leaving you cranky and tired. Avoid white flour, wheat, and foods that contain gluten, which cause inflammation and break down into sugar in the body. Choose naturally satisfying and nourishing foods to balance your emotions and assist with emotional stress. Drink herbal tea containing St John's wort, ginseng and damiana. Speak to a qualified herbalist about taking supplements for hormonal balance.

ROOM ODOURS

If you wish to eliminate the smell of stale smoke, damp, cooking or pet odours firstly you need to naturalise the environment. This is done by opening windows and doors, allowing fresh air to flow through for as long as possible. Pour vinegar into small bowls and place throughout the space. Sprinkle bicarbonate of soda onto the carpets and floors, and leave it for a few hours, then vacuum. Lemon, eucalyptus, orange and tea tree oils consistently used in a vaporiser, or oil burner freshen the scent of the room. You can also place a dash of the same oil blend in a bucket of hot water and mop the floors for the same effect.

HEAD LICE

Using a 250ml liquid soap-free base blend 15 drops of tea tree essential oil, 10 drops of lavender essential oil, and 10 drops of penny royal extract. Massage thoroughly into the scalp and hair, and leave for half an hour before rinsing with cold water. Repeat for three days. Wash all clothes and bed linen in the mixture. Use a water, tea tree, cedarwood and lavender essential oil spray daily to avoid a further plague.

SUNBURN

Initially you must treat the skin using cooling, water based creams, as applying oils may contribute to further burning of the skin. Creams containing German chamomile, lavender and neroli essential oils in a base of calendula, cocoa butter, aloe vera and marshmallow root are highly soothing. Drink loads of water and chamomile tea to internally hydrate and soothe. Take cool baths using a combination of goat's milk, oatmeal and lavender flowers. Use a body spray of witch hazel and lavender water. For best results refrigerate all creams and sprays for the additional cooling benefit. After two days of treating the burns, start an intense skin repairing regime by using rosehip, evening primrose, wheatgerm and frankincense oils.

SORE MUSCLES

Ingesting a supplement of magnesium, combined with a long soak in a hot Epsom salt bath works a treat in alleviating a tired and sore body. After a shower or bath, use a remedial massage oil or balm that contains pure essential oils of clove, ginger, lavender, pepper, eucalyptus or peppermint. Wintergreen and arnica topical ointments will help to alleviate muscle pain, bruising and ligament damage.

CLOVES AND COOKING

When cooking with whole cloves, stab the cloves into a vegetable or fruit to ensure they emit that wonderful clove flavour without wandering into the dish. Cloves have many therapeutic and nutritional benefits and are a warming addition to both sweet and savoury dishes. Suck on a few cloves if you have a toothache or sore throat.

Natural thickening agents for food and skincare

Kudzu, agar agar, xanthium gum, pectin, sago, vegetable gum and tapioca can all be used to thicken sauces, stews and desserts in cooking. These ingredients are also used for thickening creams and gels when making natural skincare products.

To stop bleeding

Apply turmeric root or powder to wounds to stop excessive bleeding. Apply a drop of pure lemon essential oil to shaving cuts and minor bleeding scratches.

Rheumatism and arthritis

Start by eliminating all wheat, gluten, refined sugar, processed food and alcohol from your diet, because these things produce inflammation in the human body. A drink with a ratio of 10ml of apple cider vinegar to 15ml of water before meals assists with inflammation. Follow a strict diet of fresh, natural and alkaline foods, use a topical ointment containing ginger, clove, thyme, lavender, wintergreen and rosemary pure essential oils, and ingest magnesium and fish oil supplements daily.

Grapefruit seed extract

Also known as citrus seed extract, this amazing liquid remedy is known to treat a spectrum of conditions including Bali belly, stomach virus, parasites and candida. Take two to three drops in a cup of purified water twice a day.

Mouth ulcers

Rub garlic, turmeric and ginger root on the ulcer for a natural antibiotic treatment. Use salt water and lavender oil mouth rinse to keep the area clean, and eliminate sugary, spicy and salty foods that cause further irritation. Stress, low immunity, teeth and gum problems may be underlying reasons for the condition.

Skin cancer prevention

Eat turmeric on a daily basis, as it is one the most powerful anti-cancer foods nature has given us. Grate up fresh ginger root, mix in some warm water and enjoy every morning on an empty stomach. Pure frankincense essential oil greatly oxygenates skin cells and may prevent the development of cancerous cells. Add 10 drops to 100ml of apricot kernel oil and use on the body and face daily.

Natural sun protection

Seek out natural and organic sun cream products. Commodities containing non-nano zinc oxide are generally effective. Jojoba, coconut and avocado oils provide very mild sun protection and are not effective enough for long periods spent in the Australian sun. Health food stores will often stock a range of natural sun creams.

Make your own cough syrup

Honey and onions both hold antibacterial properties; in addition onions contain a sulphur compound that reduces bronchial constriction. Chop up either a red or white onion into a bowl and cover with organic raw honey; allow it to sit in a warm room for eight hours. Strain the onion from the syrup and have a teaspoon every two hours if you're an adult. Children should consume a teaspoon every four hours.

Thrush

The old natural yoghurt and a few drops of pure tea tree oil on a clean tampon always works a treat. Repeat this three times per day for six days. Have warm sitz baths using one tablespoon of apple cider vinegar and four drops of pure lavender essential oil. Eliminate all dairy, refined carbohydrates and sugar from your diet. Avoid miso, chocolate, nuts and acidic foods for a few days. Restore your pH balance with organic vegetables, soups, seafood, brown rice, water and green juices.

Foot fetish

Taking care of your feet is one of the most important ways to keep the body healthy. The feet have 26 bones that support the entire body. Spend a little time each day giving your feet a little rub; use a massage oil blend that contains patchouli, vetiver and sandalwood pure essential oils to emotionally ground you. Get yourself a reflexology chart and take note of the sore parts, as tender points on the feet are an indication of problems in the body.

PMS – Pain and moodiness syndrome

When it's that time of the month the best thing you can do is nurture your body, mind and spirit. For mood swings and cramps consider taking daily organic evening primrose oil, macca powder, and magnesium and vitex supplements. Ask an aromatherapist about blending you up a concoction of jasmine, lavender, rose and clary sage pure essential oils to rub into the stomach and lower back as needed. Do not use this oil if you think you may be pregnant.

The Hangover

Drink dandelion tea and water until lunchtime, as this will stimulate the liver and gallbladder, allowing the body to detoxify from the previous evening's pollution. Spend the rest of the day eating wholesome nutrient-dense foods and resting. Taking a mega B vitamin supplement will restore nutrients that have been depleted, and taking a St Mary's thistle supplement will support liver function. Drinking a juice of fresh young coconut, turmeric and grapefruit will cleanse and hydrate you quickly, assisting your speedy recovery from this self inflicted punishment.

Crocodile skin

Apply 100 per cent pure organic oils and creams containing jojoba, coconut, olive, apricot, almond, avocado, rosehip, shea, cocoa, sunflower, macadamia or grape seed oil to alleviate super dry skin. Eating more nuts, seeds, avocados, olives, evening primrose and flaxseed oil, fish and seafood is also beneficial. Taking a practitioner grade fish or cod liver oil supplement might be worth looking into. In Traditional Chinese Medicine it is said that excessive dry skin indicates the body is too yang and requires balance with its yin energy.

HANDSTANDS

Do a daily handstand to improve blood circulation and build arm and shoulder strength. Inverted poses that reverse gravity have a wide range of health benefits, leaving you feeling energised and looking fresh faced. Find a solid wall, either in or outdoors, and hold your handstand for one to two minutes. Do a few sets, ensuring you take it easy if you feel a little dizzy.

NAUSEA

Can be caused by many things such as stress, pregnancy, motion sickness, constipation and gallbladder problems. Drinking ginger, spearmint and peppermint tea will ease feelings of sickness; acupuncture, homeopathy and reflexology also help with assisting nausea symptoms. Burning pure essential oils of lime, lemon, orange or mandarin with a drop of ginger can profoundly alleviate feelings of nausea.

SIESTA

This should be a mandatory universal practice, and in many countries this is the cultural norm. Siestas are highly valuable in countless ways; in addition to supporting heart health and alleviating moodiness and depression, an afternoon nap will support with the overall replenishing of the body's physical and emotional energetic fields, leaving you feeling revitalised and rejuvenated.

HERPES SIMPLEX VIRUS TYPE 2 – (HSV-2)

HSV-2 usually causes outbreaks around the genitals. To prevent outbreaks you must always keep your immune system in tip top condition. Consistently take additional vitamin and mineral supplements like vitamin C, E and A, zinc, magnesium and fish oils. Lemon balm and liquorice root herbs can be applied topically or ingested in tea or tincture forms. Bergamot essential oil diluted in pure coconut oil is an effective topical treatment for both herpes viruses.

ANXIETY AND PANIC ATTACKS

Last but not least, anxiety and panic attacks are one of most common human health related issues of today, affecting males and females of all ages all over the world. It is important to know we are in this together, feelings of worry and stress are normal and there are things we can do to help. For panic attacks, place 10 drops of rescue remedy under the tongue. Use massage oils that contain lavender, geranium and chamomile pure essential oils and apply after bathing. These can be rubbed into your neck, chest and stomach whenever you feel stressed. Remember to take long deep breaths as you do so. Ask a health professional about taking a practitioner grade vitamin B supplement to help with stress management.

CHAPTER THREE

FOOD RECIPES

"I would like to suggest that all the produce you use when cooking the following recipes is organic and locally sourced. It is especially important that when eating meat, poultry or any animal product that it is certified organic or certified free-range."

AROMATHERAPY FOOD SAFETY RULES

- Essential oils must be certified organic ensuring they come from a 100 per cent pure and reliable source, especially if they are being used for cooking and ingesting. You know essential oils are legitimate when they have a stamp of certification, botanical name and use-by date clearly printed on the label

- Start by using only one drop of essential oil at a time in cooking, ensuring not to overwhelm the recipe. A meal will be ruined if too much essential oil is added to the formula.

- Although essential oils are natural, they can be toxic to the system if used in excess or incorrectly. Note that not all essential oils can be ingested. Some oils are considered hazardous, and several essential oils may not be appropriate for everyone depending on your health status and constitution, especially if you are suffering with high blood pressure, epilepsy, cancer or diabetes

- Always store essential oils and aromatherapy products in a cool environment, away from sunlight so their therapeutic properties are not compromised.

- Pregnancy – Some essential oils should not be used by women who are pregnant or lactating, and an authoritative resource or an experienced aromatherapist should be consulted before using any of them. Because of uterine stimulation or possible toxicity, always use a low dilution of essential oils during pregnancy.

BREAKFAST

VANILLA-BEAN GRANOLA

Serves 4

"The best things in the world can't be seen and touched; they must be felt with the heart."

Vanilla-bean was once considered a gift from the gods. With its heady, warm and heavenly taste and fragrance it is easy to know why. The pod of vanilla is native to Mexico and is rather expensive, as in most parts of the world, it must be pollinated by hand. After being picked the pod must be dried for many months to achieve its true flavour potential. A natural partner to cream, desserts and skincare, I was fascinated to know vanilla is a natural anti-emetic, which means it assists with nausea. Dates are very rich in natural fibre, and they also possess heaps of other essential nutrients, like calcium, sulphur, iron, potassium, phosphorous, manganese, copper, and magnesium. No plant is as intertwined with Middle Eastern culture as the date palm, and dates have been enjoyed for centuries.

Apricot kernel oil contains high amounts of essential fatty acids and is also rich in vitamins A and E, which are necessary for healthy hair, soft skin and healing.

3 cups quick oats
3 cups boiling water
½ cup raw almonds
1 cup shredded coconut
2 tbsp sunflower seeds
1 cup chopped pitted dates
1 tsp crushed sea salt
1 tsp grated palm sugar
¼ cup raw honey
¼ cup apricot kernel oil
2 vanilla pods (cut in half and scrape out all seeds and flesh inside)
1 drop vanilla essential oil
1 tbsp cinnamon

Preheat the oven to 200°C. Place all the ingredients into a large bowl. Pour in two cups of the hot water and thoroughly mix this nutritional symphony using a wooden spoon. Spread the mix into a large baking dish and bake for 10 minutes. Add in the third cup of water, stirring thoroughly through once again. Bake for a further 10 minutes.

AWESOME WITH
Serve your hot granola in a dessert dish with cold coconut or almond milk. Garnish with a little more shredded coconut and honey. Keep your left over mixture refrigerated in a container and enjoy any time of the day. The mixture should last for a week or so.

ATMOSPHERE
This warm bowl of love is best enjoyed on a chilly winter morning, in front of the fire with a blanket and a book. Set a good enough scene? Burn vanilla and gardenia essential oils for their sweet, floral and feminine aroma, making you feel nourished, safe and warm.

BREAKFAST MUFFINS

Makes 1 dozen

"Happiness is about being non-judgmental, accepting, flexible and present in the moment."

Use the wondrous health benefits of ancient grains and a variety of nutritionally abundant ingredients, to create a batch of the most moist and hearty muffins that leave you feeling well nourished and complete. These breakfast muffins have just the right mix of textures and flavours, not to mention the perfect synergy of dietary fibre and complex carbohydrates.

2 cups kamut flour
½ cup amaranth flakes
½ cup oat bran
1 mashed banana
2 free-range eggs
½ cup buffalo ricotta
¼ cup sunflower oil
½ cup currants
½ cup coconut sugar
¼ cup ground sunflower seeds
¼ cup sesame seeds
¼ cup walnuts
¼ cup maple syrup
3 tsp gluten-free baking powder
2 tsp cinnamon powder
½ tsp sea salt

In a frypan at medium heat fry off the walnuts in a tablespoon of maple syrup until golden and set aside to cool. Preheat the oven to 200°C. In a large bowl, combine the flour, amaranth, oat bran, baking powder and salt. In a separate bowl, thoroughly mix all the other ingredients – the mashed banana, ricotta, eggs, coconut sugar, cinnamon, sunflower oil, maple syrup, currants, sunflower and sesame seeds. Combine all the ingredients, including the maple syrup walnuts, thoroughly together using a wooden spoon in the large bowl that originally contained the flour. If the mixture is too moist add a little more oat bran, if too dry add a little more yoghurt or soy milk.

Spoon a generous amount of the muffin mixture into lightly oiled muffin tins; we want these muffins to be large in size. Sprinkle the tops with coconut, sesame and sunflower seeds. Bake for 25 minutes. After 15 minutes check your muffins with a knife to make sure it doesn't come out sticky, as this means they are uncooked. Serve your breakfast muffins in a basket at a table decked out with a few natural jams and spreads and a hot pot of ginger tea. Munching out on these super healthy muffins at breakfast time will ensure a prosperous day full of energy and abundance.

BROWN RICE BREAKFAST

Serves 2

"In the morning do something pleasant and nourishing for yourself and then the whole day will take care of itself."

Congee is a type of rice porridge popular in many Asian countries. It is a regular breakfast of savoury or sweet white rice cooked until it turns mushy and soup-like. It is an inexpensive meal that provides the body with energy and life force, proving to be a healthy and traditional way to the start the day. My brown rice version is slightly modern, yet still captures the many flavours of healthy fresh food. Brown rice is a wonderful source of dietary fibre, and bananas have just the right amount of potassium and vitamin B12 to keep you pumped for the entire day. Almonds contain generous amounts of vitamin E, considered essential in the treatment of many diseases of the circulatory system.

1 cup brown rice
6 cups water
1 banana
¼ cup acai berries
¼ cup dried cranberries
¼ cup crushed dry roasted almonds
1 tsp coconut sugar
1 tbsp honey
1 tsp Himalayan rock salt
2 tbsp shredded coconut

Add one cup of brown rice and four cups of water to a rice cooker or saucepan, and bring to the boil. Stir. Turn down and simmer for one hour. Add the final two cups of water and stir, and once again bring to boil. Add the sugar and salt, and simmer for another 45 minutes. The consistency now should be somewhat similar to porridge – if at any time you feel things are looking a little gluggy, just add a little more water, stir and simmer. Easy! When you're ready, scoop into a nice big bowl and garnish with thinly sliced banana, acai berries, cranberries, almonds, and honey, then sprinkle the shredded coconut, with love. I always add a teaspoon of evening primrose or flaxseed oil to my breakfast, but that's your call. The variation for a savoury style congee would be to ditch all the sweet ingredients and use poached chicken, a boiled egg, lemongrass, coriander, garlic, tamari soy and then garnish with shaved coconut, fresh lemon and chilli flakes.

ATMOSPHERE

Mornings are a time for reflection and stillness. Burn eucalyptus and rosemary essential oils to endorse clearness of mind and body. Freely play some of your favourite meditation music. Whilst you eat your breakfast have a note pad and pen close by and try to strategically plan your day, either with a point form list of tasks or perhaps a diary style entry. This is a great way to start the day. When we have vision, we have direction, and then follows a drive to achieve everything we truly desire.

GF MUFFINS

"You can have all the ideas in the world, but without love and passion you have nothing."

I owe my thunder thighs to muffins. One day I actually read the ingredients on the pack of a typical blueberry muffin I picked up from the petrol station. My eyes were darting over words and numbers I couldn't even understand, along with a long list of emulsifiers, raising agents, refined sugars and sweeteners, milk powders, 155, E171 and many other food additives. Below is a recipe for home-made chunky muffins that are real, healthy and contain ingredients your body would like to process. And trust me they taste good, so good in fact I think I'll have another one...

1½ cups rice flour
1½ cups quinoa flour
3 tsp gluten-free baking powder
1 cup rapadura sugar
5ml vegetable glycerine
½ cup rice milk
½ cup nuttlex spread (dairy free butter)
2 eggs, beaten lightly
1 drop lemon essential oil
1 organic carrot
1 small tin pineapple chunks
½ cup shredded coconut
½ cup crushed walnuts
½ cup organic sultanas
1 pinch sea salt

ICING
1 lemon wedge
1 tbsp raw honey
1 cup soy cream cheese
1 tsp of walnut oil

First up, using a little plant butter, grease each muffin hole. In a large bowl sift in the flours and baking powder. Now throw in the wet ingredients, the melted butter, rice milk and eggs. Carefully mix. Grate in the carrot and add the pineapple chunks, sultanas, coconut, sugar, salt, lemon oil, walnuts and anything else that you think might be amazing. Mix everything together very thoroughly. Once combined, spoon the mixture into the muffin tray holes. Fill one or two holes with water to keep the muffins extra moist. Bake at 180°C for 25 minutes, or until fluffy and a little golden.

OH YES IT HAS ICING!
Thoroughly mix together 200g of soy or tofu cream cheese, 1 tbsp honey, 1 tsp of walnut oil and a squeeze of lemon. Allow to sit in the fridge for one hour before dolloping upon your muffin top!

ATMOSPHERE
Take along the GF muffins to a friend's baby shower or kitchen tea. Don't tell anyone they are gluten and dairy free, until they are all finished; the guests may be pleasantly surprised. The GF muffins are great in the morning with coffee or earl great tea. Burn bergamot and rose essential oils to make you happy, and spearmint oil for digestion, just in case you eat too many.

ISRAELI EGGS, ON LITTLE EVELEIGH STREET

Serves 4

"Balance is not letting anyone love you less than you love yourself."

A meal rich in culture and flavour, a complete powerhouse of protein, antioxidants and dietary fibre and I am happy to share that butter beans are abundant in the best sort of fibre – soluble fibre that helps to eliminate cholesterol from the body. It is very important to keep blood cholesterol levels stable as this will ensure a healthy and happy heart. Cinnamon is further added to stabilise blood sugar levels for the day, and the grated ginger gives depth and warmth to the flavour, as well as assisting with digestion.

4 fresh free-range eggs
6 overripe roma tomatoes
A few handfuls baby spinach
1 cup water
1 can butter beans
1 red chilli
1 drop lemon essential oil
1 organic garlic clove
2 shallots
2 tbsp olive oil
1 tsp honey
½ tsp ground cinnamon
½ tsp grated ginger
A little parsley
1 tsp sea salt
1 tsp cracked pepper
1 loaf fresh sourdough bread
100g Israeli hummus
1 avocado

Heat the olive oil at medium temperature in a big, deep frypan. Once the oil is warm throw in your diced tomatoes and cup of water, followed by the white beans, finely chopped garlic, shallots and chilli. After two minutes, stir in the spinach, honey, cinnamon, ginger, lemon oil, parsley, salt and pepper. Bring to the boil. Now, make four small spaces in your aromatic bean mixture, as this is where you will crack your four eggs. Once the eggs are resting in the concoction, you can turn the heat down to simmer and wait for the eggs to poach. Serve one egg and a few tablespoons of your mixture onto two pieces of fresh or toasted spelt sourdough bread. Finish with a good dollop of hummus, a scoop of avocado and a squeeze of fresh lime.

ATMOSPHERE

I picture that this meal would be thoroughly enjoyed for brunch, eaten at a little picnic table in a courtyard area or on a balcony space. Set up this space with plenty of blankets and books so you and another can happily set up camp for a few hours, enjoying the comforts of beautiful food and company. Experience feelings of clarification and self-realisation by burning frankincense, lemon and basil pure essential oils.

BUCKINGHAM STREET BANANA BREAD

"You can't always get what you want... But sometimes you get what you need."

Bananas are extremely high in potassium, which helps normalize the heartbeat and regulate the body's water balance. During periods of high stress, our body's potassium levels tend to become depleted. Cinnamon is the epitome of spices. In Traditional Chinese Medicine it is used for colds, flatulence, nausea, diarrhoea, and painful menstrual periods. Believed to improve energy, vitality, and circulation it is most useful for people who tend to feel hot in their upper body but have cold feet.

1 cup buckwheat flour
1½ cups spelt flour
1½ cups almond meal
1 cup almond oil
1 tbsp coconut oil
3 overripe mashed bananas
1 ripe banana
3 tsp gluten-free baking powder
2 free-range eggs
2 tbsp goat yoghurt
½ cup honey
¼ cup rapadura sugar
1 cup crushed walnuts
1 tsp cinnamon
1 tbsp stevia liquid
1 pinch sea salt

Preheat the oven to 200°C and, with a little olive oil, grease your baking tray. In a large bowl, cream the almond oil with honey, fold in the eggs, almond meal, cinnamon, stevia, sugar, salt, coconut oil and the mashed overripe bananas. Now sift through the buckwheat and spelt flours and the baking powder, chop up the ripe banana into chunky slices and throw in with the yoghurt, and walnuts. Make sure you mix all the ingredients together thoroughly, until very moist. Smooth out the mix into a medium sized, fairly shallow baking tray and pat down the mixture. If you're thinking the mixture is too dry, no worries, just add a little more oil or yoghurt. Bake at 180°C for 25–30 minutes, or until a toothpick comes out clean from the centre. Do not under bake or over bake. Keep checking your banana bread – we want this to be perfectly moist and amazing.

AWESOME WITH
In a saucepan melt off some further coconut oil, add some sliced pears, then when slightly golden, add a sprinkle of cinnamon. Feel free to casually add the syrupy pears over a slice of your toasted Buckingham Street Banana Bread, along with a scoop of ice cream, a few more walnuts and a dash of organic maple syrup and you've got yourself a pretty sensational dessert.

ATMOSPHERE
Get warm, get cosy, get comfortable and burn a blend of vanilla and cinnamon pure essential oils and enjoy the simple pleasures of life – a good book, watching a favourite movie curled up on the lounge, a warm bath or sitting outside in the garden. Life is about hard work, sacrifice and personal growth. It is also about joy, relaxation and freedom. Enjoy both sides of the coin.

OBRIGADO DIEGO –
THE MORNING AFTER

Serves 2

"Oats make you calmer. So does a little love in the morning time."

Start your day with a steaming bowl of oats, which are full of fibre, folate, and potassium. This wholesome super food can lower bad cholesterol and help keep heart arteries clean. Oats have compounds that have been shown to reduce the risk of heart disease and cancer, because they help control cell-damaging particles called free radicals. Blackberries are a solid source of vitamin E, the essential vitamin for repair. They contain salicylate, which is also found in aspirin and is thought to lower the chance of heart disease. Blackberries also contain the very necessary vitamin C, phenolic acids and folate. All in all this is a mighty healthy breakfast—make it!

1 cup of oats
1 can coconut milk
1 small can coconut cream
8 pecans
6 dried pitted dates
A few fresh blackberries
A few fresh blueberries
2 tbsp honey
1 tsp cinnamon
1 tsp flaxseed oil

Add the oats, a little water and the coconut milk to a saucepan and cook on high until boiling. Throw in the dates, turn down the heat to low and simmer for five minutes or until semi-gluggy, but not too thick. Serve into your favourite breakfast bowls and top with the fresh berries and chopped pecans to create an attractive heaped pile. Drizzle with honey, sprinkle with cinnamon and flaxseed oil, and add a dollop of coconut cream to conclude – Delicioso, saboroso.

Atmosphere

Enjoy on a Saturday morning after a big week of work and play. Oats contain carbohydrates that are absorbed slowly, and this enhances the serotonin-producing abilities of your brain. Serotonin is your body's own stress-relieving chemical, so the rest of your Saturday should be a mellow one. Freely burn sweet orange and ylang ylang pure essential oils that will assist with anxiety and encourage you to feel content, safe and supported. Play some classical music that is believed to slow down the heart rhythm. Now get ready for a relaxed weekend.

DATE SPREAD

"In this life we cannot always do great things, but we can do small things with great love; making jam is one of them."

It's a real struggle to find jams and spreads that aren't packed with sugar and additives, so sometimes you have to take matters into your own hands and make your own. I have chosen to use dates as they are naturally high in their own natural sugars and are used to invigorate the spleen and stomach, helping those with constipation, poor appetite and fatigue. Dates are a splendid fruit that nourish the blood and benefit those suffering with anaemia. You can also use dried figs, apricots or prunes.

500g dried pitted dates
Boiling water
1 sterilised glass jar

Throw your dates into a saucepan, cover with boiling water and crank the heat up to high. Allow to boil for five minutes. Stir. You will notice the water has reduced rather quickly and the dates have started to become very mushy and stringy. Cover once again with boiling water; reduce the heat and let the mixture simmer for around half an hour to 45 minutes. Allow to cool, and then using a clean spoon, scoop into an airtight large glass jar.

AWESOME WITH
Date spread is gorgeous on all kinds of sweet and savoury toasted breads. You can also use the spread to add to cake mixture, curries or dollop onto porridge and muesli. Your date spread should last refrigerated for two weeks. Enjoy.

LUNCH/DINNER

AKI ADZUKI BEAN CASSEROLE

Serves 4

"Courage is the prize life gives for releasing fear."

Macrobiotically, this is a perfectly balanced meal, using ingredients that assist in restoring the adrenal glands in order to stabilise your physical and emotional health. The body systems often become depleted when the kidney qi is low, leaving you feeling lethargic and unenthusiastic about life. The kidneys are the body's batteries and we need to do things to recharge our batteries. Autumn is a time of harvest, signalling it is time to prepare for winter by eating nourishing and healthy meals just like the adzuki bean casserole. Seaweed, pumpkin and adzuki beans are all extraordinarily rich in mineral elements that provide immense nutritional benefits. They contain large amounts of dietary fibre, minerals and trace elements, including iron, potassium, calcium, folate and iodine, as well as vitamins A, C and B-complex.

ATMOSPHERE
This dish is beneficial for replenishing the kidneys and the spleen, so send these organs your loving energy with every mouthful. Always eat your meals in a comfortable and peaceful environment in the company of those you enjoy. Burn or vaporise marjoram, sandalwood and Roman chamomile pure essential oils to reduce mental stress and help release fearful emotions.

¼ cup olive oil
1 large onion
3 crushed garlic cloves
1 tsp grated ginger
1 cup adzuki beans (soaked overnight)
1 organic butternut pumpkin
6 shiitake mushrooms
½ cup arame seaweed
1L natural vegetable stock
1 tsp sea salt
1 tsp cracked pepper
3 tbsp tamari soy sauce
1 tbsp tamarind paste
1 drop organic ginger essential oil
1 bunch coriander
1 bunch Italian parsley

Soak the arame seaweed in a bowl of purified water for 10 minutes prior to cooking. Wash the pumpkin and mushrooms. Thinly slice the onion and mushrooms and chop the pumpkin into even cubes – it is okay to leave the skin on the pumpkin as this holds the most anti-parasitic properties. Sauté the onions in olive oil until soft, add the crushed garlic and grated ginger and cook for a further minute. Include the adzuki beans, pumpkin, mushrooms, seaweed and stock to the pot and bring to the boil. Lower the heat and add the drop of ginger oil, tamarind, tamari, salt and pepper. Thoroughly stir and simmer for one hour or until the beans are soft.

This casserole is good served with brown rice or quinoa, or cooked in individual baby pumpkins that have been baked in the oven with the seeds removed. Garnish with some fresh coriander and parsley, cracked pepper and a good squeezing of fresh lemon juice.

A MIDSUMMER NIGHT'S – SALAD

Serves 4

"A good meal should give vital energy and a physiological boost. You ought to feel the positive effects of all the foods you eat."

The midsummer night's salad is a light meal that is ideal and easy to prepare, using carefully selected ingredients that nurture and detoxify. The salad is abundant in purifying and liver-cleansing bitter foods that are naturally high in healthy salts, which help to restore nutrient absorption and mineral balance. Watercress is a type of brassica vegetable that helps fight free radical damage in the body and has the ability to help fight cancer. Watercress is also high in iron, folate and vitamins A and C, which support the formation of red blood cells.

1 bunch watercress
1 bunch sunflower sprouts
100g rocket
2 tbsp fresh tarragon
1 organic avocado
1 organic pear
8 marinated artichokes
10 pitted large green olives
¼ cup pine nuts

Wash, chop and throw together. Really, that is pretty much it! Thoroughly rinse your greens, and set aside to drain. Transfer the washed greens to a large salad serving bowl. Slice the avocado in half and scoop its creamy goodness freely all over your awaiting greenery. Thinly slice the artichokes, pear and olives and tenderly

scatter over the salad. Toss in the pine nuts, a few cracks of sea salt and pepper, garnish with chopped tarragon and you're ready to add the dressing. Baked fish or chicken make a great partnership with this sweet, salty and perfectly balanced summer salad.

DRESS ME IN...
½ cup olive oil
¼ cup lemon juice
½ tsp honey
½ tsp ground mustard seeds
¼ tsp ground black pepper

Add all the dressing ingredients to a small glass or ceramic bowl and stir until they are thoroughly combined and the lemon juice and the olive oil completely emulsify.

AN AUSSIE GIRL'S CHINESE

Serves 4

"Why try and be like someone else, when you can be the best version of yourself?"

One of the most beautiful things about cooking is gaining inspiration from other cultures, modifying the recipe and creating your very own perfect version. A handful of cashews can be equivalent to taking a Prozac. When I was a young girl and my mum ordered us Chinese, I always got the chicken cashew nut. There is something really satisfying about the combo of meat, nuts and rice. One night I decided to make a super healthy MSG free version. My housemate Maria was the guinea pig. Maria was impressed.

400g sliced organic chicken
1 cup rice bran oil
1 chopped broccoli head
½ cup sliced pineapple
1 bunch Chinese spinach
1 tbsp grated ginger
1 tbsp grated garlic
5 cm fresh red chilli
100g salted cashews
1 cup water
1 tsp kudzu powder
¼ cup rice bran oil
1 tbsp tomato paste
2 tbsp maple syrup
2 tbsp tamari soy sauce
1 tbsp apple cider vinegar
1 handful fresh mint
1 tsp sea salt
1 tsp black pepper

Place one teaspoon of kudzu powder and one cup of water in a small bowl and thoroughly combine using a teaspoon – this mixture will act as a natural thickening agent to your stir-fry and Kudzu is beneficial for the entire digestive system. In a heated frypan goes the rice bran oil and then your sliced up chicken pieces. After a few moments, add the garlic and ginger. Stir around until the chicken is pretty much on the white side of life. Now would be the time for the broccoli, chilli, pineapple, tomato paste, maple syrup, apple cider, tamari sauce and the kudzu mixture. Turn up the heat to high and allow the flavours to unite for a minute or two. Time for the cashews to make an appearance, along with the spinach, salt and pepper. Turn down the heat to low and thoroughly stir. Allow to simmer for 10 minutes before serving. Dish up in Chinese style eating bowls on top of white or brown rice; garnish with a little more tamari soy sauce and a few fresh mint leaves. Eat with chopsticks.

ATMOSPHERE
If you're feeling like being a good healthy kid enjoy this with hot Chinese oolong tea, as it is great for weight loss and just might help break up the good fats in the cashew nuts. If you're feeling indulgent, enjoy with a clean dry sauvignon blanc. We ate this outside in our courtyard one warm January night. For some reason we had the *Dirty Dancing* soundtrack playing and it made us think about our early years. It's nice to reflect on your past. It reminds us of where we are going...

FOOD ENVY

Serves 4

"Eat high quality food often; as the food you eat becomes you."

If this meal was brought to you in a restaurant, it would be the kind of dish that would have everyone in the room turning their heads, wishing they ordered the same. Not only is this meal aesthetically beautiful, presented as a four storey vegetarian tower of colour, but it is a perfectly crafted meal that caters to all daily dietary requirements. It has the right amount of sweet and delicious ingredients that provide you with vitamins A, B and Cs, leaving you feeling satisfied and sparkling with joy. Note that if you cannot get purple sweet potatoes you can use carrots for the mash, and you can roast turnips for the base.

2 large sweet potatoes
2 large purple sweet potatoes
1 pineapple
½ Spanish onion
1 bunch bok choy
1 bunch coriander
100ml coconut oil
1 lime
1 tsp sesame seeds
½ tsp cinnamon
1 tsp ground sea salt

Slice up the orange sweet potatoes and pineapple into medium thick circular slices. Place the sweet potato pieces into an oven tray, drizzle with a little coconut oil and sprinkle on a pinch of sea salt. Roast at 180°C for 15 minutes until the sweet potato is slightly tender and still firm. Open the oven and include four pineapple cylinders to the tray of roasting sweet potatoes and roast for a further five minutes. Whilst the sweet potato and pineapple are roasting, thinly slice the purple sweet potato and place into a vegetable steamer and cook for 20 minutes until soft. Remove and place into a deep glass bowl and add a tablespoon of coconut oil, a pinch of sea salt and a little cinnamon. Mash the purple sweet potato mix until it is smooth and creamy. The final step is to thinly slice the bok choy and Spanish onion and then fry off in a saucepan at medium heat in a little coconut oil, cinnamon powder and the sesame seeds until the bok choy is wilted and soft and the onions are caramelised. By this time the sweet potatoes and pineapple are roasted and ready for you to arrange the first layer of a pineapple circle followed by the second layer of a few sweet potatoes circles to the centre of clean white plates. Evenly distribute a large dollop of the purple mash to the top of each stack, and conclude the art work by draping the bok choy and onion gently over the mash. Garnish with a squeeze of fresh lime, a sprinkle of sea salt, a little fresh coriander and a teaspoon of coconut oil. Trust me, this meal is worth the effort!

ATMOSPHERE

This meal is symbolic of good health, happiness and the sweet moments in life. Enjoy it with friends and family sitting as a group at a table, using a knife and fork so you can carefully dissect each sweet layer and say things like, "Oh my goodness this is amazing." Burn rose and orange essential oils to foster lasting feelings of inner joy and love for humanity, food and this wonderful world we live in. Chanting a few om shantis in gratitude for the peace in your life and the wish for peace in the lives of others is a beautiful thing to do, too.

THE FRIDAY NIGHT COOKING CLASS

Serves 4

"It is nice to be good, but it is great to be nice.

The perfect winter curry for a perfect winter's night that takes 10 minutes to prepare, 10 minutes to cook and 40 minutes to simmer. In less than an hour you've got yourself a really nice, creamy, deliciously authentic Indian curry baby! This cosy curry will keep you going all winter with its notably high quantities of protein, antioxidants, and vitamin A and antibiotic properties, making it a solid dinner for people with a sore throat or in need of a good hit of immunity boosting nutrients.

1 medium can chickpeas
2 organic carrots
1 zucchini
½ small pumpkin
½ cup olive oil
1 white onion
100g English spinach
3 cloves organic garlic
3 overripe roma tomatoes
1 medium can organic coconut milk
1 medium can organic coconut cream
1 cup water
2 tsp fresh or powdered turmeric
1 bunch fresh coriander
2 tsp curry powder
1 tsp raw honey
1 tsp chilli powder
2 crushed cardamom pods
1 tsp fennel seeds
1 tsp sea salt
1 pinch cracked pepper
1 cucumber
1 small tub goat yoghurt

Pour your olive oil into a largish frypan, crank up the hot plate to medium, throw in the sliced pumpkin, carrot, zucchini, garlic, onion and fresh turmeric, a little water and stir-fry until semi-golden. Stir. In about 10 minutes the vegetables should start to become tender. Add the coconut cream, coconut milk, water, chickpeas, roma tomatoes, spinach, curry powder, turmeric, honey, pods and seeds and last but not least the sea salt and pepper and thoroughly stir. Bring the heat to high for two minutes, allowing the spices to unite properly with all the curry ingredients. Stir through and turn the heat to low and simmer for about 40 minutes until the curry is thick, fragrant and creamy. Serve with basmati or long grain brown rice.

AWESOME WITH
A dollop of goat yoghurt that has thinly sliced cucumber stirred through it. Tear up some fresh coriander and add this and a squeeze of fresh lemon over the top of your steaming hot curry.

ATMOSPHERE
This cosy curry should be served in a deep bowl and be eaten with a spoon. We all ate ours crossed-legged on the floor surrounded by plenty of blankets and pillows. Having Bollywood movies and music playing in the background is a very cool and entertaining thing to do, especially for a meal like this. Orange and black pepper pure essential oils are the best choices to have burning to support the joy and warmth of this dish. Additional candles scattered throughout the home are a nice touch too.

GADO-GADO

Serves 4

"Food is our common ground, a true universal experience."

Tempeh is the national food of Indonesia; it gently takes the satisfaction of vegetarian heartiness to the next level. Protein-abundant it is, ultimate flavour is why we love it. Tempeh can be crunchy or tender; either way it rocks in salads, pastas, stir-fries and curries. Today we use it in a salad so healthy and mouth-watering because it is fresh, crisp and sweet you will feel that each taste is too good to be true.

1 organic iceberg lettuce
1 cup bean sprouts
200g tempeh
4 biodynamic eggs
1 Spanish onion
8 cherry tomatoes
1 mango
1 bunch coriander
½ cup rice bran oil
1 tsp chilli flakes
1 tsp sea salt
1 tsp ground black pepper

Begin the ceremony by mindfully chopping all the precious tempeh into cube style chunks. Boil your eggs for 10 minutes. Thinly slice the onion and mango and set aside. At a high temperature heat up all the rice bran oil in a small frypan, throw in the tempeh, sea salt and pepper and toss about. After two minutes reduce the heat to medium. It important to properly cook tempeh until it's perfectly golden and crisp. Turn down the heat and remove the tempeh. Add a little more rice bran oil to the frypan and two or three handfuls of bean sprouts. Cook until soft. Prepare a few individual bowls of washed and finely chopped lettuce and tomatoes, then add the tempeh and bean sprout mixture, sliced eggs, onion and mango. Smother in peanut sauce and conclude with a decent sprinkle of chopped coriander.

For a warm style gado-gado, you may use water spinach instead of lettuce and some steamed vegetables and rice in place of the mango and onion.

THE PEANUT SAUCE:
4 tbsp 100 per cent natural crunchy peanut butter
1 tsp 100 per cent natural chilli paste
1 tsp 100 per cent natural garlic paste
1 tsp grated palm sugar
A dash organic tamari soy sauce
A dash coconut milk
A dash boiling water
A squeeze fresh lemon

Thoroughly mix all the sauce ingredients together until a perfectly smooth and creamy consistency is achieved. Drizzle over your salad and enjoy. Keep the peanut sauce in mind for future roasted vegetables and satay dishes.

HAMBURGERS FOR GIRLS

Serves 6

"If you wish to be respected by others, then you must first respect yourself."

Oh food, glorious food! This mighty hamburger recipe encompasses highly nutritional, fresh and wholesome ingredients specifically selected for strength and stamina, so you can chase the boys all day long! Oregano essential oil has great value as an antiseptic and is also very effective against candida overgrowth in the body.

500g organic lamb mince
1 can adzuki beans
1 small brown onion
2 eggs
1 clove crushed garlic
1 bunch parsley
1 drop oregano essential oil
½ tsp dried rosemary
1 tsp sea salt
1 tsp cracked pepper
100g goat fetta
1 cup rocket
6 fresh spelt hamburger buns
½ cup olive oil

Thoroughly rinse and drain the adzuki beans. In a large bowl thoroughly combine the mince, adzuki beans, the eggs, chopped onion, garlic, oregano essential oil, all the herbs and salt and pepper. Refrigerate for one hour before shaping the mince mixture into patties. Place the patties, covered, in the fridge for an hour before cooking, as this will help them to firm. At medium temperature, heat some olive oil on a clean barbeque hotplate or in a large frypan and add your patties. Cook on each side for 10 minutes; flip if you want to cook for a little longer. It's best to have the frypan heat at low to medium, so they cook all the way through and don't burn on the outside. Serve a patty or two onto toasted bread or fresh rolls. Garnish the hamburgers with rocket, a generous scoop of the chutney, crumbled up goat fetta and a few cracks of black pepper and wallah!

OH, DID I MENTION WE HAVE CHUTNEY?

Raisins have a profound relationship with tomatoes and they contain a type of iron called nonheme iron. This makes them great to eat with meat and high vitamin C foods as this helps our bodies to absorb the iron in meat, so let's use them in chutney.

1 red onion
1 garlic clove
1 organic leek
1 punnet cherry tomatoes
½ cup water
¼ cup raisins
1 tsp cinnamon
1 tsp pepper
1 tsp Celtic rock salt
1 lemon

Chop up ya onions, garlic, leek and cherry tomatoes quite finely. Heat up some olive oil in a medium frypan. Add the onions, garlic, leek and cherry tomatoes followed by the water; bring to boil until things start to bubble. At this point throw in the raisins, cinnamon, pepper, salt and a good squeeze of lemon juice. Stir, bring to a low heat and then simmer for half an hour. The chutney consistency should be a little mushy and stringy; it will keep for two to three days.

ATMOSPHERE

When I was creating this meal all I could think was, how rad would this be for a girl's BBQ! Get all your besties together for a Sunday afternoon backyard BBQ cook off. Serve your hamburger on eco friendly paper plates; get a good grip, pick it up and just go for – it gets messy but it's worth it. Wash down the burger goodness with cold Coronas and lime wedges. Burn lemon scented eucalyptus and bush mint pure essential oils to remind your guests of plant life native to the greatest land on the planet, Australia! Dig out those scratched old school Aussie pub cds, play cards, sing, play cricket or just drink beers and mellow out. Aaahhh, Sunday sips!

KIYO

Serves 6

"I know a woman who has taught me about hard work, dedication and how to make the best soup in Japan! Her name is Kiyo."

I love this meal in winter because it is full of warm, healthy and protein repairing ingredients. I took Kiyo's soup back to Australia after my last visit to Japan and my family were completely blown away by how deliciously tasty it was. This recipe feeds up to six, so if you want to make it smaller just use less of the ingredients, or why not make it massive and freeze it for yourself all winter long!

Tofu has been a part of the Asian diet for centuries and is rich in many nutrients that include calcium, proteins and iron. Miso, made from soybeans is medicinally a bit like yoghurt, containing many healthy bacteria and enzymes that make miso great for keeping the gut flora nice and healthy. I have to say how absolutely mad I am for enoki mushrooms, especially since I discovered they are the greatest carbohydrate-free alternative to pasta.

250g silken tofu
250g firm tofu
500g organic chicken
½ cup rice bran oil
200g enoki mushrooms
100g shiitake mushrooms
100g oyster mushrooms
1 organic leek stalk
1 bunch Chinese or mustard spinach
1L soy milk
1L purified water
2 tbsp miso paste
2 tbsp tamari sauce
½ cup sake or rice wine vinegar
1 tbsp ground sea salt
¼ cup toasted sesame seeds

Wash all your vegetables thoroughly. In a large and quite deep saucepan or hotpot heat the rice bran oil then add the sliced chicken and sauté until ever so slightly until golden brown. Reduce the heat to medium and throw in the chopped up tofu and leek. Gently stir. After a few moments, pour in the soy milk, miso paste, sake and salt. Stir thoroughly. After two or three minutes follow with the water, tamari sauce, spinach and all the different mushrooms. Note that it is not necessary to slice the enoki mushrooms, but you will need to cut off the base, one centimetre from the root. Bring the stove top to a high heat and allow all the flavours to merge, keep stirring all the ingredients thoroughly. After five minutes reduce to a low heat, and allow the mixture to just relax and simmer for around 15 minutes. Ladle your soup into ceramic Asian-style bowls. Eat with chopsticks and have spoons handy, in order to lap up the soy milk sensation effectively. Garnish with toasted sesame seeds, pickled cabbage, coriander and a little chilli if you like things nice and warm.

ATMOSPHERE

Burn geranium, lime and basil pure essential oils for mental clarity, balance and spiritual awareness. Kiyo's soup is best enjoyed crossed-legged at a floor table setting, in the company of friends and family. Feel open to play a few Zen meditation tunes in the background, as you send the universe gratitude for this exact moment...

LENTIL AS ANYTHING

Serves 6

"Wholefood cooking is all about real food in its natural state, that has the ability to heal, nourish and delight."

Proteins, dietary fibre, folate, amino acids, iron... I could dead set ramble on about lentils all day! Legumes have been a part of the human diet since the beginning of time and today are greatly respected as the vegetarian's primary protein source. One chilly winter afternoon I made a decision that a whole meal needs to be dedicated to the humble lentil. The outcome is a truly wholesome, inexpensive meal that tastes incredible.

2 cups dry red lentils
1 cup brown rice
1 cup quick oats
1 white onion
1 organic grated carrot
1 cup frozen peas
1 cup crumbled goat fetta
3 free-range whisked eggs
¼ cup all natural tomato paste
¼ cup all natural barbecue sauce
½ cup olive oil
3 organic garlic cloves
½ bunch Italian flat-leaf parsley
2 tsp dried mixed Italian herbs
1 tsp roasted paprika
1 tsp ground sea salt
1 tsp ground black pepper

Wash and soak the lentils and brown rice in a large soup pot for one hour. Begin the cooking by simmering the lentils and rice combination in water until tender; this will take about 45 minutes to an hour. Drain thoroughly, and set aside. Thinly slice the onion and garlic, then sauté in a little olive oil for three to five minutes. You will need a pretty large bowl in order to combine the sautéed onions, grated carrot, peas, dry oats, crushed garlic, olive oil, tomato paste, barbecue sauce, goat fetta, eggs, salt, pepper, paprika, parsley and dried herbs with the lentils and rice successfully. You'll notice that there are a lot of ingredients in this bowl, so be sure to mix this wholefood extravaganza together very well.

Once the ingredients are thoroughly combined, firmly press this mixture into a lightly greased deep bread loaf style oven pan. Drizzle the top of the loaf with a lashing of barbecue sauce and add a sprinkle of oats. Cover with foil and bake for one hour at 180°C. Check your loaf after half an hour to ensure it is cooking superbly; remove the foil for the remaining half an hour of the cooking time. Take out your lentil loaf from the oven and allow it to sit and slightly cool before serving, as this will help the lentil loaf to firm up. Slice up into thick chunky slices and serve with mashed potato and mashed peas along with gravy. If by chance your lentil loaf turns out sloppy, it's all good, just have it shepherd's pie or stew style – either way it will still be amazingly delicious and tremendously healthy!

The necessary gravy recipe

10 button mushrooms
1 white onion
2 tbsp tapioca flour
1 cup soy milk
1 tbsp olive oil
1 tsp ground salt and pepper
A little fresh chopped sage
A little fresh chopped thyme

Thinly slice up the mushrooms and onion; throw 'em in a small saucepan and gently sauté at a medium heat. Add all the other ingredients and bring to the boil allowing the herbs to unite with the soy milk and flour. Make sure you continually stir until boiling point. Now bring to a simmer allowing your gravy to thicken. Serve in an old school gravy pot.

Atmosphere

A hearty Sunday evening family dinner is what this is. Prepare for an early dinner by setting the table for the entire family and placing the lentil as anything loaf and gravy smack bang in the middle. Have a separate bowl of the mashed potatoes and another bowl for the mashed peas close by, so everyone can just dig in and help themselves. In summer the lentil as anything would be lovely served with a garden salad. Burn clary sage, basil and lemon pure essential oils to stimulate the throat chakra and ensure the whole family communicates and listens well to one another.

MANAO
Serves 6

"A dish that completely captures Thailand: the flavour, freedom and culture."

Every time we eat we have got to be supported by health sustaining ingredients. Out of all the healing herbs, garlic contains compounds that have been shown to lower cholesterol levels and high blood pressure, two of the leading risk factors for heart disease. The mixture of fish pieces adds excitement and diversity to this dish, not forgetting that fish holds nutrients that are high in good quality proteins and omega-3 fatty acids. Kaffir lime leaf adds an unmistakable, refreshing taste that is essential in Thai cooking. It gives that special flavour blast. The kaffir lime is believed to brighten a person's mental outlook and even ward off evil spirits. In folk medicine, kaffir lime juice is used to promote healthy gums and teeth.

6 pieces mixed fish fillets; snapper, perch, ling and barramundi are best
1 young coconut
2 tbsp coconut oil
2 tbsp 100 per cent natural fish sauce
1 cup button mushrooms
2 organic leeks, trimmed, cut into short, very thin strips
2 tbsp lemongrass paste or powder
4 red chillies finely chopped
1 cup coriander, finely chopped
1 cup Thai basil, finely chopped
2 garlic cloves, crushed
3cm grated ginger
3cm grated galangal
1 tbsp palm sugar
1 lemon
1 tbsp grated lemon rind
½ a Spanish onion
2 limes
2 kaffir lime leaves
3 cups organic jasmine rice

Wash and slice up all the vegetables and herbs. In a saucepan fry off the leeks and mushrooms in a little water and coconut oil at a medium heat. Remove when things turn a little golden and perfectly mushy. Set aside to cool. Chop the top off the coconut and add its flesh and water into a fairly deep ovenproof ceramic dish. Stir in the lemongrass, chilli, coriander, basil, kaffir lime leaves, garlic, ginger, galangal, palm sugar, grated lemon rind, fish sauce and one tablespoon of lime juice. Add the fish fillets and the leek, onion and mushrooms mixture to the ceramic dish, making sure you mix around the fish fillets thoroughly amongst all the glorious flavours. Cover and refrigerate for 30 minutes. Preheat the oven to 180°C. Remove the dish from the refrigerator and cover with foil. Cook for 25 minutes or until the fish and vegetables are tender. Spread the cooked jasmine rice over a large serving platter; follow by spooning the fish and vegetables evenly across the rice and platter. Complete by pouring over the delicious marinade, a squeezing of lime and lots of chopped Spanish onion and coriander.

ATMOSPHERE

Prepare this meal on a bamboo place mat along with small Asian-style eating bowls and chopsticks so your guests may help themselves. In four separate little bowls have plenty of sliced lime and lemon wedges, chilli paste, crushed ginger, garlic and soy sauce, as this makes a great extra garnish combination for those people who love to add heaps of aromatic flavours to their food. Dress up your table with a colourful, silk runner. Place votive candles down the centre of the runner. Create a centrepiece of orchids, exotic flowers and river stones or polished pebbles. Burn frankincense and kaffir lime essential oils for spiritual evolvement and energetic purification. Get in the mood by playing some traditional style Thai music, dance around and immerse yourself in the beautiful culture of Thailand.

MISS WALTER SALAD

Serves 4

"Your beliefs don't make you a better person, your behaviour does."

My dear friend is always creating these deliciously warm and fragrant salads, and her love for a good hearty salad has inspired me. I have chosen sweet potato as the heart of the salad, an old vegetable that is a powerful source of dietary fibre and vitamins A and C. Out of all the green vegetables rocket is up there with the healthiest, and certainly enhances any salad, proving to be a top source of calcium, iron, manganese, copper and potassium. The Miss Walter Salad is full of herbaceous goodness. Herbs do much more than just enhance the flavour of a dish, they have been used since ancient times to prevent infection and relieve pain and bodily discomfort. This scrumptious salad is a light yet satisfying meal to make for a few favourite friends. If some of your guests are of the male kind you can always serve with a good steak or some grilled chicken.

2 large sweet potatoes
1 Spanish onion
10 cherry tomatoes
120g rocket
½ cup raisins
½ cup walnuts
60g goat fetta
3 handfuls green beans
1 tbsp black sesame seeds
¼ cup olive oil
A little thyme
A little coriander
A little basil
1 tsp dill tips
1 tsp ground sea salt
1 tsp cracked pepper

Roughly chop the sweet potato and place in a shallow oven tray with a little olive oil, salt, pepper and water. Place in the oven at 200°C. I often use a little water when baking vegetables so they don't dry out. The sweet potato takes about 30 to 40 minutes to cook, therefore be mindful of timing if you want to serve it straight from the oven to the salad. Now in a frypan heat the oil and fry off the green beans along with the black sesame seeds, until slightly golden. When the sweet potato is about five minutes from being cooked (you will know this by pricking with a knife and feeling that it is tender) start to prepare the rocket, chopped onion, herbs and tomatoes by tossing together in a large salad bowl. Throw in the sweet potatoes and green beans. Lovingly garnish the top of your salad with raisins, walnuts, goat fetta, dill tips and the dressing.

THE DRESSING
¼ cup extra virgin olive oil
¼ cup balsamic vinegar
½ cup lemon juice
½ tsp ground pepper

Add all of the above dressing ingredients to a clean glass bottle, and shake it baby! Done.

ATMOSPHERE
Night time, loads of white wine, fairy lights and Spanish guitar music. Hopefully I just painted the perfect picture for the evening we had the night before I left for Japan. Good friends, good food, good times... To support the festivity feel free to burn a synergy of ylang ylang and lime essential oils, these aromas also enhance creative and sexual energy.

MORE THAN A MEZZE PLATTER

Serves 6

The best kind of love is the kind that makes you a better person, without changing you into someone other than yourself."

There is nothing sexier than the feel of the body of someone with healthy smooth skin. If you are not genetically blessed with supple and soft skin that produces abundant skin nourishing oil, then you have to take matters into your own hands and start eating your way to sexy skin. Historically, high quality olive oil, rich in antioxidants is considered one of the best ways to keep the heart and body healthy. The Mediterranean diet is a timeless dietary movement that Western nations can learn from.

THE OIL INFUSION
A little fresh marjoram
A little fresh sage
A little fresh basil
6 red organic grapes
6 garlic cloves
8 peppercorns
2 cups Spanish extra virgin olive oil
½ cup aged merlot
¼ cup 100 per cent natural
balsamic vinegar

Wash the grapes and herbs. Using a sharp non-serrated knife, start chopping the herbs by using a rocking motion from the knife tip back towards the handle. With the flat side of the knife flatten out the grapes, garlic and peppercorns. Transport all the ingredients into an airtight glass bottle or cruet; add the olive oil, wine and balsamic. Turn upside down a few times and allow to ferment for two days prior to the making of the mezze plate.

1 red capsicum
4 giant Russian garlic cloves
1 zucchini
1 eggplant
¼ pumpkin
12 large green olives
100g goat cheese
100g buffalo mozzarella
6 artichokes hearts
8 small dolmades
1 tub Israeli hummus
1 small bunch red seedless grapes
1 tsp salt
1 tsp pepper
1 fresh organic fermented sourdough loaf
A two tier serving platter

To begin the preparation for this ultra lavish mezze platter, you will need to wash all the fruit and vegetables, de-skin, de-seed and thinly slice up the capsicum, zucchini, eggplant and pumpkin – aim to slice the pumpkin into boat style slices. Preheat the oven to 180°C and place the vegetables in a shallow baking tray and add salt, pepper, and a good lashing of the specially prepared oil infusion. Don't forget to add the giant garlic cloves and bake with their skin on. Place the vegetables in the oven uncovered for 15 minutes and then suss them out, give them a stir, add a little more oil and place them back in the oven now at 200°C. The aim of the game is to cook the vegetables until they are soft and a little crispy and golden. This may take a further 20 minutes. Please keep an eye on the vegetables, observing the cooking process every five to ten minutes. In the meantime, arrange your desired serving platter by spreading out in individual piles the remaining fresh ingredients of the green olives, goat cheese, buffalo mozzarella, artichokes hearts, dolmades, Israeli hummus, red seedless grapes and sliced bread. Once the vegetables are perfectly roasted they too will be added in individual piles to the serving platter. Add lemon wedges separately between the piles of ingredients and garnish with paprika and fresh herbs.

MUSSELS MEK–ICO

Serves 6

*"Come on baby light my fire...
quite often good food and a
good love will do this."*

Cook on a warm Saturday afternoon for good friends and family. This soup is so jam packed with vitamins and minerals, I don't really know where to begin, but I'll give it a crack anyway... Mussels are renowned for being an excellent source of iron and zinc, both important for healthy blood and skin. Most seafood contains phosphorus, folic acid, iodine, calcium and vitamin B12, so you will be bouncing off the walls for days. Mussels Mek–ico was inspired by a friend of mine, and was slightly adjusted just so I could call it my own. Enjoy, we certainly did.

1kg mussels
14 green prawns
500g ocean perch
8 ripe tomatoes
1L hot water
1 cup tequila
3cm grated ginger
6 cloves organic garlic
2 chillies fresh, paste or powdered
1 bunch coriander
A few basil leaves
6 limes
2 tbsp sea salt
1 tsp black ground pepper
2 tsp tamari soy sauce
Olive oil

First chop your tomatoes into cubes, place on an oven tray and drizzle with olive oil, sea salt, pepper and basil. Place in the oven on high for about half an hour or until really juicy. Wash, clean and de-beard your mussels using cold water; de-shell and slice 1cm down the back of your prawns and cut the ocean perch into thick uneven chunks. Now set all the seafood aside.

Heat some oil on high in a small frypan. Chuck in the prawns and chopped ginger – they will only need 30 seconds tops; the objective of this is not to fully cook the prawns, but rather to ensure they butterfly. Set aside the prawns. Get yourself out a really large wok or saucepan and heat up on medium high. Add a little olive oil and the garlic, stir in the oven roasted tomatoes and water; feel free to add more water if it is not soupy enough. Quickly follow by adding tequila, tamari soy sauce and chilli. Stir. Okay, so now the time has come to throw in the mussels, prawns in ginger and fish. Turn the heat down and simmer for no longer than 10 minutes, as seafood is not so good overcooked. Tear up the coriander and squeeze in two of the limes giving the meal some final life force. Prepare your eating environment, as it is essential Mek-ico mussels are served super hot.

ATMOSPHERE

Put a place mat in the centre of a big old table, along with soup spoons. In three separate bowls place some lime wedges, sea salt and fresh coriander. Pour some good tequila into shot glasses for your guests, and shoot back a few – lip, sip, suck with lemon and salt – normally only the crazy will throw back, as tequila either really agrees with you, or not at all. Light some candles, play some pleasant Latin American background music, burn rose, lemon myrtle, mandarin and ylang ylang pure essential oils to promote joy, love and celebration. Don't be surprised if all the tequila, aphrodisiac essential oils and zinc foods make you want to shag all night, just roll with it and enjoy your life!

OKRA HEALTH STEW

Serves 4

The journey must be one of discovery and observation. Participate in the culture rather than judge it."

The okra health stew contains ingredients that offer an abundance of immunity-boosting, cell-nourishing and body-cleansing powers. Cook this wonderfully tasty stew at the start of winter to ward off illness and restore your body when it's feeling depleted. Healthwise okra does a little bit of everything. It holds a key compound that attacks and prevents cancer by hampering the effects of free radicals, which cause cell damage, and it offers a complete range of vitamins and minerals to the body. When cooked, okra releases a thick, slimy fluid that not only serves as a fantastic source of nutrients, but acts as a natural thickening agent in cooking, making it great to use in curries and soups.

12 okras
1 large eggplant
8 roma tomatoes
1 bunch kale
1 large can kidney beans
¼ cup rice bran oil
2 cups purified water
4 organic crushed garlic cloves
4 cm grated organic ginger
1 onion
4 cm grated organic turmeric
1 bunch coriander
1 bunch flat-leaf parsley
1 tbsp Himalayan rock salt
1 tbsp propolis honey

Begin by washing and roughly chopping up all the vegetables and herbs. In a large saucepan gently heat the rice bran oil along with the thinly sliced onion, ginger and garlic; sauté for a minute or two before adding the beloved chopped okras. Stir. Incorporate the tomato, kale, eggplant, kidney beans, fresh herbs, grated turmeric and garlic, water, salt and honey and bring to a high heat for five minutes, ensuring all the ingredients come together. Allow the stew to simmer for one hour before serving with brown rice or quinoa.

Although okra is from the summer crop, if you can get your hands on some late autumn it makes for a great pre-winter cook off. Make enough of the okra stew to eat a little at every meal for two days ensuring the required nutrients build up in the system preparing the physical and emotional body for any health and immunity setbacks pre-winter solstice.

POACHED CHICKEN PERFECTION

Serves 4

"Imagination is everything. It is the preview of life's coming experiences. The true sign of intelligence is not knowledge but imagination."

Make this sweet fresh salad during the spring time, as spring represents new beginnings, healthy changes and preparation for the summer celebration. The pomegranate is indeed a romantic, sexy and traditional fruit. A well known super fruit, it is not only high in nutrient-dense antioxidants, it has the ability to affect cell and molecular structure, and the potential to be anti-ageing and beneficial for overall health. Pomegranates are at their peak from summer to autumn. My good friend Masayo tells me that Japanese women eat them to encourage a healthy reproductive system.

1 whole chicken
2 pomegranates
4 garlic cloves
100g mixed rocket and lettuce leaves
8 fresh figs
½ cup crushed walnuts
100g goat fetta
1 tsp black sesame seeds
1 bunch fresh basil
1 tsp raw honey
1 cup olive oil
1 tsp sea salt
Cracked pepper
1 loaf rye bread

Put the good quality chicken into a large pot. Cover with water, add a few peppercorns, a teaspoon of sea salt and a couple of crushed garlic cloves and you're ready to roll. Bring it all to the boil and then simmer for about an hour. Trust me when I say you are going to get the most perfectly moist cooked chicken to add to your salad. Wash and cut the figs in half and place the halves onto a tray, along with a dash of olive oil, a sprinkle of sea salt, a drizzle of honey and grill for 10 minutes, or until golden and tender.

In a large serving bowl add your mixed rocket and lettuce leaves, followed by the warm pulled apart chicken slices. Now the fun part begins. Cut the pomegranate up into quarters and starting to flick out the little juicy sweet balls onto the salad, follow by the baked figs, crumbled fetta, crushed walnuts and basil. Conclude by garnishing the salad with black sesame seeds, cracked pepper, tahini dressing and quite possibly an extra lashing of extra virgin olive oil. Whilst you are decorating your salad, place the loaf of crusty rye bread in the oven at a low heat for five minutes to warm through.

SIMPLE YET EFFECTIVE DRESSING
½ cup tahini
1 lemon

Spoon the tahini into a cute little bowl, squeeze in the lemon and stir until smooth. Tahini is a nutritional powerhouse. No joke, it's high in vitamins E and A as well as vitamins B1, B2, B3, B5, B6, and B15. Wow!

RENDANG

Serves 4

"Honour your physical, spiritual and emotional being. Remember that rest and recovery are essential to human vitality."

Rendang is a warm and joyful meal to get the blood flow moving and reju-venated. Organic red meat is high in iron and packed with immune-boosting ingredients. Lemongrass is a good in-ternal cleanser that helps to detoxify the liver, pancreas, kidneys, bladder and the digestive tract, that cuts down uric acid, cholesterol, excess fats and other toxins in the body while stimulating digestion. Ginger has great anti-cancer and immune system enhancing proper-ties. It is also one of nature's best antibiotic sources and is sometimes referred to as the universal healer.

4 beef shanks
2 tbsp rice bran oil
3 cups water
1 large can coconut cream
¼ cup shredded coconut
1 large white onion
4 organic garlic cloves
2 fresh red chillies seeded and sliced
2 cm grated ginger root
1 tsp powdered turmeric
1 tsp powdered galangal
1 tbsp raw honey
2 whole cloves
1 tsp star aniseed powder
1 tbsp paprika
1 lemongrass stalk tied into a knot
1 drop lemongrass essential oil
3–5 kaffir lime leaves
1 tbsp Balinese salt
2 tsp grated palm sugar

¼ cup tapioca flour
2 cups brown rice

Pre-coat the beef shanks in tapioca flour, and refrigerate them for half an hour. Heat a little rice bran oil in a frypan and add the beef shanks, onions, garlic, ginger, and shredded coconut; gently stir for about three minutes on a medium heat. Transfer to a slow cooker, and add the water, coconut cream, honey, turmeric, paprika, galangal, kaffir lime leaves, knotted lemongrass, cloves, star anise, chilli, palm sugar and salt. Using a wooden spoon, carefully combine everything together. Allow to cook slowly for about four to six hours, ensuring the meat is nice and tender and has absorbed all the incredible flavours. This dish should be semi-thick in texture, creamy, fragrant and sweet. Serve each shank and some rendang sauce on top of a bowl of hot brown rice, then garnish with shredded coconut, a squeezing of lime and fried shallots.

ATMOSPHERE
This dish is a great one in the colder months, due to the tremendous warm-ing combination of chilli, ginger, onion, lemongrass and clove. Reinforce the household warmth by burning lemon-grass and black pepper pure essential oils to capture the fragrant aroma of Indonesia that warms the soul and gladdens the spirit.

SUNDAY FETTUCCINI

Serves 4

"Eating well gives a spectacular joy to life and contributes immensely to kind and happy beings. Eating is of great importance to the spirit."

Sunday is without a doubt a great day for amazing food and for fuelling our bodies with nutrients prior to a week of hard work. The Sunday fettuccini happens to be a perfect meal if you're feeling like something rich and hearty but without the saturated fats or heavy dairy. The people of Japan pretty much eat fish every day, and it is not a coincidence that Japan is one of the most innovative countries in the world. Salmon in particular has an almost perfect essential fatty acid profile crucial for brain and behavioural health.

250g spelt fettuccini pasta
250g salmon fillets
1 cup water
1 to 2 cups good quality extra virgin organic olive oil
A few handfuls baby spinach
A small tub goat curd
100g oyster mushrooms
½ white onion
1 bunch fresh dill
1 tbsp capers
1 drop lemon essential oil
1 tsp Celtic rock salt
1 tsp ground black pepper
1 lemon
1 tsp grated lemon rind

Start by washing the mushrooms, spinach, dill and lemon. In a saucepan cook the spelt fettuccini for two minutes less than its recommended cooking time, rinse with cold water and set aside. In a largish frypan heat up half-a-cup of olive oil, then turn down the heat to medium and carefully place in the salmon and water. After a minute or two, flip the salmon and throw in the thinly sliced onion and mushrooms. Delicately stir until slightly golden brown. After five minutes turn down the heat to low, and now carefully break up the salmon into medium sized chunks using a wooden spoon. Thoroughly stir in the pepper, salt, lemon rind, spinach, capers, lemon oil, the cooked pasta and some more olive oil along with the tub of goat curd – this will add a really gentle creaminess to your pasta. Stir through for a moment or two. Throw in some fresh dill and bring the heat down to low for five minutes before serving. Squeeze some fresh lemon over the pasta, a little more fresh dill, a few cracks of fresh ground pepper and a dash more of olive oil. Serve in big shallow bowls, and eat with a fork and spoon.

Atmosphere

The Sunday fettuccini is great at lunchtime, with or without white wine. Enjoy with a big group of friends by double or tripling the above ingredients. This dish deserves to be eaten outside in the sun, along with some lingering sweet Italian tunes in the background. Feel free to deck out the outside table Italian style and serve the fettuccini with some good crusty bread and a fresh garden salad. Chew softly and enjoy the delicate, creamy saltiness of the pasta. Feel full, content and ready for an amazing week ahead – Bello.

THE BEETROOT AND SALMON ONE

Serves 2

"All you have to be in this life is grateful, honest and kind. Everything else will pan out from there."

The brilliant beetroot delivers a nutritional résumé of many, many vitamins and minerals such as beta-carotene, folate, potassium, vitamin C and iron that are awesome for the kidneys and rebuilding the liver. Salmon just steals the show for being super high in omega-3 fatty acids, crucial for human existence and are accountable for many physiological processes in the body, including fertility, immunity and communication between cells.

2 salmon fillets
2 beetroots
2 carrots
1 cup green beans
3 garlic cloves
½ lime wedge
1 tsp sea salt
Infused olive oil
A hint paprika
A few walnuts
1 tub 100 per cent natural hummus

Preheat the oven to 180°C. Chop up the carrots and beetroots into smallish pieces and slices. Don't cut up the garlic, as it is best to eat roasted garlic out of its skin. Place the salmon, carrots, garlic, and beetroot and walnuts in an oven tray or dish, and drizzle with about three tablespoons of your favourite infused olive oil and about one teaspoon of paprika and

sea salt. Place in the oven uncovered and wish it well. In 45 minutes the salmon will be hot, moist and pink, and the vegetables will be delightfully crunchy. In a saucepan bring some water to the boil and blanch the green beans for a few minutes. Serve the salmon on top of the roasted vegetables and beans along with a dollop of good quality hummus and a squeeze of fresh lime.

ATMOSPHERE

Cook on a Friday night, as the next day is skinny jeans Saturday! The beetroot and salmon dinner is low in carbohydrates and has loads of liver-cleansing properties that aid in detoxification, hence it's great for cellulite. Eat sitting up straight with a knife and fork. Chew slowly and feel free to appreciate every mouthful of the nutrients. Burn lavender, frankincense and cypress pure essential oils to enhance intuition and enlightenment; these oils are recommended for spiritual maturity and new beginnings.

THE PERSIAN INFLUENCE

Serves 4

"Some of the best moments are spent with friends dancing, drinking and eating. The way to get to know a country and its culture is through its food."

If I had to describe this dish I would say... a thick, rich, hearty casserole of tender lamb, immersed in a sweet melody of perfect pumpkin and plump prunes. A Zen shiatsu master once told me to eat a small amount of lamb each day for a week, if you want to build courage, strength and raise iron levels. Prunes have a reputation as one of nature's best laxatives. They are especially high in insoluble fibre, making them a great remedy for keeping your digestive system on track. I really have a deep love for pumpkin – the taste and the texture. Pumpkin is so good for you; it's super high in beta-carotene and iron.

500g diced lamb
½ cup olive oil
1½ cups water
1 small organic pumpkin
200g baby spinach
1 onion
100g pitted prunes
1 small can tomato paste
1 tsp cinnamon powder
1 tsp dill tips
1 tsp fenugreek powder
1 tsp honey
1 tsp sea salt
1 tsp ground black pepper
1 tsp saffron threads
1 tbsp slithered almonds
3 cups basmati rice

Chop up the pumpkin, lamb and onion into cube style chunks. Heat up a fairly large frypan and add your olive oil. Throw in the lamb, pumpkin and onions and stir-fry at a medium heat for three minutes. Add the water, spinach, tomato paste, cinnamon, dill tips, fenugreek, prunes, honey and finally the salt and pepper. It's a good idea at this point to turn up the heat for a minute or so and thoroughly stir to allow all the flavours to successfully combine. Allow to simmer for one hour.

You can also make this using lamb shanks. Place all the ingredients in a casserole dish and cook in the oven at 100°C for three hours.

AWESOME WITH
A big bowl of yellow saffron rice, garnished with slithered almonds and a good squeeze of fresh lime. Saffron by weight is more expensive than gold, so enjoy this indulgence with a good bottle of Iranian Shiraz which is simply superb with this meal. If it's an alcohol-free day, a saffron tea will be fine.

ATMOSPHERE
I made this dish on the first day of autumn, it was a rainy Monday afternoon and I decided to take some time out for myself. I recommend having a hot bath using one drop of nutmeg and two drops of mandarin essential oils in a teaspoon of almond oil to keep warm and positive. Rent out that movie you have been meaning to watch, and stay indoors on a comfortable lounge under a warm soft blanket. Have an early night and be sure to wake up feeling recharged and courageous.

THE PLANT PROTEIN STIR-FRY WITH AN EGG

Serve 4

The healthiest approach to life is laughter."

Did you know eggs are one of the only foods that contain vitamin D? Vitamin D is an important vitamin for helping the body absorb calcium. This is a good meal to create when you need a night off the carbohydrates because it is filled with proteins that provide your body with these building blocks we call amino acids, which are necessary to maintain the health of your muscles, organs and immune system. The nutritional value of this plant protein stir-fry makes it a sensational meal for immunity, strong vision, healthy skin, sturdy bones and blood formation.

250g spongy firm tofu
1 can butter beans or any white beans
½ cup olive oil
3 free-range eggs
½ head broccoli
1 burdock root
1 fennel
2 cups baby spinach leaves
1 large garlic clove
1 white onion
2 ripe tomatoes
½ cup chopped coriander
¼ cup tamari soy sauce
1 tbsp honey
1 tbsp sesame seeds
1 tsp Himalayan rock salt
1 tsp cracked pepper

Prior to cooking, slice up the tofu into cubes and set aside to marinate in a little tamari soy sauce, honey, sesame seeds, salt and pepper for one hour. Commence by washing and finely chopping up all the vegetables and herbs. Heat up some olive oil in a large frypan and add the finely chopped up marinated tofu, the broccoli, fennel, burdock, onion and garlic. Turn to a medium heat and very gently stir-fry. I suggest this because broccoli is fragile, containing many remarkable nutrients, including vitamin C, beta-carotene, folic acid, calcium and fibre, so it is best treated delicately. After about 10 minutes add the chopped tomatoes, butter beans, salt, pepper and water. Now throw in the coriander and finally crack in the famous eggs. Turn up the heat to high for two - three minutes and stir continuously until the eggs have happily scrambled amongst the plant life. Then simmer for a further five minutes.

AWESOME WITH
A drizzle of sesame oil, a sprinkle of sesame seeds and a splash of naturally brewed soy sauce. If you are feeling like something hearty, brown rice or thick rice noodles are a great addition to the plant protein stir-fry.

ATMOSPHERE
This vegetarian delight should be eaten early evening and is best served in small bowls and eaten slowly with chopsticks, ensuring you properly digest all the goodness of this meal. Burn fennel and spearmint pure essential oils to further assist with digestion and increase intellectual clarity.

TURMERIC SPREAD – AKA TUM CASH

"When you find peace within yourself, you learn to live in peace with others."

Be careful, because this spread is so scrumptious it can become addictive, and you will talk yourself into having it with every meal. Eating macadamia and cashew nuts decreases cholesterol levels and supplies the body with many nutrients that impact favourably on human health. Although tum cash is lavish, it is a healthy alternative to margarine and butter because it is abundant in healthy fats, vitamins and minerals that leave you feeling nourished and satiated.

1 cup raw cashews
1 ½ cup raw macadamias
1 tbsp turmeric powder
½ cup organic coconut oil
½ cup olive oil
1 tbsp ground Himalayan rock salt

Place all the ingredients in a food processor or blender and process until smooth. This will take a minute or two, and you will need to stop and scrape down the sides occasionally. Once blended, spoon the tum cash into a clean glass airtight jar and keep refrigerated for two to three weeks. Enjoy with fresh or roasted vegetables, spooned over salads or smeared across savoury and sweet toasted breads.

WINTER SOLSTICE SOUP

Serves 4

The Winter Solstice symbolizes the rebirth of the light and the divine spark within us all."

A creamy synergy of hearty vegetables, infused with mandarin oil to warm the body and strengthen immunity. Take pleasure in the winter solstice soup during the colder months, as it is abundant in grounding and nurturing ingredients. Mandarin essential oil is very toning on the system and encourages weight loss, cleansing the body from accumulated toxins. In traditional medicine, cassia cinnamon is used for colds, flatulence, nausea and painful menstrual periods. It is also believed to improve energy, vitality, and circulation.

2 large sweet potatoes
4 carrots
1 onion
2 garlic cloves
2 cm fresh ginger
1 tsp cinnamon powder
1 tsp sea salt
1 tsp ground black pepper
1 tbsp rice bran oil
4 tsp tamari soy sauce
2 tsp cashew butter
1L filtered water
1 bunch flat-leaf parsley
1 bunch coriander
1 drop organic mandarin essential oil
50ml coconut cream
1 tbsp sesame seeds

Chop up the sweet potatoes and carrots. Thinly slice the onion, ginger and garlic. In a soup pot style saucepan heat up some rice bran oil and add the onion, ginger and garlic. Stir at a medium heat until golden. Turn the heat to low and add the water, sweet potatoes and carrots. Bring to a boil for 15 minutes. Turn down the heat once again to low. Tear up the coriander and parsley and add together with the salt, pepper, tamari, cashew butter and cinnamon powder. Stir and allow to simmer for at least half an hour. Transfer all the ingredients to a large blender or food processor and blend for two minutes. Conclude by thoroughly stirring in the mandarin essential oil. Serve in shallow soup bowls. Garnish with ground sesame seeds, a dash of coconut cream and chopped fresh herbs. Enjoy with toasted bread or rice.

WINTER WONDERLAND

"The winter is a season for rest and reflection."

When I'm in the mood for a little winter detox and also want to clear out my fridge, I often whip up these creamy and delicious soups that can be made using almost any vegetables: cabbage, celery, broccoli, kale, carrots, spinach, beans, pumpkin, artichoke, leek, cauliflower, tomato, eggplant, coriander, basil, thyme, dill and parsley. The best ingredient choices for a great soup are always fresh and organic. When you are detoxing, the last thing you want are vegetables that have been sprayed with pesticides. All my soups take less than an hour to make, and create about six bowls, a perfect amount for a one person, one day detox. These are my favourite combinations so far.

THE ENERGY SOUP

1 butternut pumpkin
3 carrots
1 large head broccoli
6 roasted garlic cloves
1 tsp cumin powder
A handful coriander
1 tsp Himalayan rock salt
1 tsp magnesium or Epsom salts

THE STRANGELY DELICIOUS SOUP

2 carrots
2 large sweet potatoes
2 potatoes
1 fennel bulb
A handful of fresh dill
1 tbsp red miso paste
1 tsp Himalayan rock salt
1 tsp magnesium or Epsom salts

This method applies for both soups. Start by chopping up all your vegetables into small cubes or thin slices. Place the chopped vegetables into a large, deep saucepan and cover one to two centimetres above with boiling water. Crank up the hotplate to high and place a lid on the saucepan. After about five minutes things will start to boil rather rapidly; remove the lid and stir. Continue to boil and cover for another 10 minutes and add any salts, herbs, paste or supplements you need (we add these late so we don't spoil the properties of these additions). Stir well. Turn the heat down and simmer for about half an hour. Remove from the heat and allow to cool for a few minutes. Ladle out the ingredients and their liquids into a blender and blend for one minute. Pour into a storage container and blend the next lot.

Both soups will keep covered in the fridge for two or three days. Feel free to freeze and add to rice, stew and casserole dishes if you get bored with eating soup all day.

DESSERTS – THE FUN PART!

AUTUMN EQUINOX

Serves 4

"Give thanks for your abundance."

The Autumn Equinox is traditionally a time to look inward, honour the planet, give thanks for the harvest, and prepare for a time of dreaming. Autumn marks the transition from summer to winter, which is a time for restoration. In a world that is often so terribly out of balance, it can be both healing and heartening to celebrate this special time. Appreciate the abundance you already have and open up to the possibilities you wish to cultivate in your life. My amazing friend Alison is one of the most traditional and creative women I know. One year she invited me to her Autumn Equinox house party. We drank mulled wine, ate delicious autumn cuisine and gave thanks for a great life.

2 green apples
2 soft pears
1 cup boiling water
1 cup red wine
½ cup raw honey
4 cinnamon sticks
1 cup chopped pitted dried dates
½ cup chopped pitted prunes
¼ cup chopped pecans
1 pinch salt
1 drop nutmeg essential oil
1 tsp nutmeg powder
2 tsp flaxseed oil

Preheat the oven to 200°C. Remove all cores from the apples and pears. It helps if you have an apple corer., but if not, all good, you can use a knife to cut them out. Make the holes about three quarters of an inch to an inch wide. In a bowl, thoroughly combine the dates, prunes, honey, cinnamon sticks, nutmeg oil, pecans, salt, red wine and boiling water. The hot water will turn the mixture sticky and syrup like. Don't forget to stop and appreciate the smells of this warm and spicy combination. Place the cored apples and pears in a baking tray. Using a long teaspoon stuff each apple and pear with the hot mixture. Drizzle the outside of the apples and pears with the left over hot sauce. Surround the apples and pears with a little more boiling water, so they don't dry out. Cover with aluminium foil and bake at 180°C for 40 minutes, or until perfectly tender but not too mushy. Remove from the oven and baste the fruits several times with the pan juices. Serve each apple and pear with a good dollop of the cold sheep's yoghurt cream, a dusting of nutmeg and a drop of flaxseed oil.

SHEEP'S YOGHURT CREAM
200g sheep's yoghurt
2 tbsp maple syrup

To make the sheep's yoghurt cream, vigorously mix together by hand the yoghurt and maple syrup in a bowl until the mixture is smooth and creamy. Refrigerate for one hour before serving. Serve the cold cream with the warm apples and pears or any dessert that you may make in the future.

ATMOSPHERE
This very spectacular autumn dessert can be made on any day with the intention to enrich your body, mind and soul. A great dessert to make for your friends and family after a home cooked traditional baked dinner. Eat in antique dessert bowls, using silver dessert spoons. Play some classical music and relax with a full stomach in a comfortable chair. Burn ginger, cinnamon and frankincense oils to feel at peace with wherever you are in life... because all is well just as it is.

HALVA

*"Nothing lasts forever.
Nothing is permanent."*

Anyone who has ever visited a Hare Krishna temple or restaurant will have undoubtedly tasted the delicious halva pudding. The memory of the comfort of the sweet, hot, fluffy and spiritually-infused comfort foodiness has never left my spirit since the first time I tasted it. It's a beautiful comforting and sweet dessert made with naturally wholesome ingredients.

2 cups water
½ cup rose water
1¼ cups rapadura cane sugar
1½ cups coarse-grained semolina
1 cup fresh pineapple pieces
1 cup sultanas
1 orange zest
100g ghee
1 tsp cardamom powder
1 tsp saffron strands
¼ cup crushed pistachio nuts

Combine the water, rose water, sugar and orange zest in a saucepan. Place over a moderate heat and stir to dissolve the sugar. Bring to boil, then reduce the heat to very low and cover with a tight fitting lid. Now, in a separate saucepan, melt the ghee over a fairly low heat, stirring from time to time. Add your semolina. Slowly stir-fry the semolina until it is golden in colour and becomes aromatic. Throw in the saffron, cardamom powder and slithered almonds. Remove saucepan from the heat and slowly pour the hot sugar syrup into the semolina mix. Return the saucepan to the stove and stir steadily over a low heat until the semolina is fully absorbed into the liquid – it will start to form into a pudding-like consistency. Now is a good time to stir in the sultanas and thinly sliced pineapple pieces. Place a tightly fitting lid on the saucepan and cook over low heat for a further two minutes.

ATMOSPHERE
Make halva for your family and friends. It is a delicious quick and easy dessert and is great after Indian or Nepalese food. Serve hot in dessert bowls as it is, or add soy custard and ice cream and garnish with crushed pistachio nuts. I especially recommend playing some Hindu music and burning clove and cinnamon oils for further comfort and encouragement.

HIGH VIBRATION BALLS

"Vulnerability is having the humility to share with another your true authentic self."

These deliciously decadent treats leave you feeling happy and well nourished, combining healthy ingredients that taste amazing. The damiana plant is native to areas surrounding the Gulf of Mexico. It has long been used as a tonic for the kidneys' and as a stimulant for the sexual organs. Damiana is excellent for balancing hormones and the nervous system. Drink damiana tea when you are feeling down, out of sorts, grumpy, angry or upset; it will give you an immediate feeling of wellbeing. Rose essential oil heightens your physical and spiritual vibration and possesses many healing benefits.

1 cup organic crunchy peanut butter
½ cup unsweetened cacao powder
or carob powder
¼ cup shredded coconut
1 tbsp maca powder
1 tsp damiana tincture
3 tbsp coconut oil
2 tbsp goji berries
1 tbsp sunflower seeds
3 tbsp agave nectar
1 drop rose absolute pure essential oil
½ tsp green stevia powder

In a large bowl, thoroughly mix together the peanut butter, coconut oil, cacao powder, shredded coconut, agave nectar, stevia powder, maca and damiana. Add the goji berries, sunflower seeds and a drop of rose oil to the mixture and gently unite. Leave the mixture to refrigerate for one hour. Using your hands and a tablespoon, make tablespoon-sized balls. Roll each ball with a little more shredded coconut. Refrigerate until firm and enjoy with someone you love, or someone you could love...

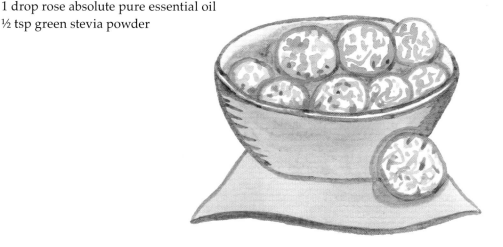

PEACHES 'N' CREAM

Serves 4

*"All you need is faith and trust...
and a little bit of pixie dust!"*

This sweet fuzzy skinned fruit is a wellness centre of health. The luscious peach is abundant in vitamin C, beta-carotene, iron, potassium and dietary fibre, making it a great immunity strengthening food choice. Peaches are always at the top of my list of organic fruits to buy because they are greatly affected when sprayed with pesticide residues. Peaches and cream is a dessert inspired by all the living pixies and fairies out there, sharing a certain mystery and elegance of their time.

3 large organic peaches
2 organic apricots
100ml orange blossom (neroli) water
1 lime
2 vanilla pods
1 tsp cinnamon
1 tbsp organic coconut oil
¼ cup chopped raw Australian macadamias
2 cups 100 per cent pure maple syrup

Heat up the coconut oil in a medium sized frypan. Wash the peaches, apricots and lime. Halve and stone the peaches and apricots. Scrape out the seeds from the vanilla pods. Place the peaches and apricots in a frypan and heat at a high to medium temperature tossing around for a moment or two, in the coconut oil. When the peaches and apricots start to turn a lovely golden colour, throw in the neroli water, maple syrup, vanilla and cinnamon. Swirl around this peachy goodness, whilst inhaling the sweet aromas. Squeeze in the lime, stir and simmer for 10 minutes. Serve the steamy hot fruit and syrup in small dessert bowls. Place a huge dollop of the cold coconut cream on top, sprinkle with crushed macadamias just as you would sprinkle fairy dust, and wish all beings including yourself peace and happiness.

THE CREAM
1 small can coconut cream
2 tbsp thick sheep's yoghurt
1 drop pure vanilla essence

Combine the ingredients in a bowl; refrigerate for one hour.

ATMOSPHERE
In the garden or local park, set up table and chairs under a shady tree. Lay out your favourite tea set and decorate with fresh and dried flowers, scented beeswax candles, glitter, fairy books and fairy photographs. Bring along a traditional candle flame oil burner and enjoy aromas of patchouli, jasmine and sweet orange pure essential oils that enhance communication and creativity. Serve the peaches and cream dessert with freshly brewed coffee or tea. Keep your eyes peeled for fairies; they just might live nearby!

SOUL KITCHEN

"Healthy cooking is all about feeding the muse and fuelling creative inspiration."

I would like to introduce you to my date loaf. It's moist, sweet and delicious. It kind of reminds me of a sticky date pudding slash pecan pie. The date loaf was magically created one rainy Saturday morning after yoga when I was feeling like something naughty but nice. Healthy sweets like this are a great way to alleviate a sugar craving without feeling guilty, so enjoy! Quinoa is starting to gain popularity and compared with all other grains, it has the highest protein content. Your body requires protein to build and repair tissues. Many of us do not get enough protein, so adding quinoa to meals is an easy and terrific idea to ensure you do. Pecans, oh pecans, I remember being a little girl and trying a bit of my Aunty Di's pecan pie and falling in love. Pecans are a guest star today in my cooking for their cholesterol lowering ability and high dietary fibre content.

2 cups rice flour
1 cup hazelnut meal
½ cup quinoa
2 tsp gluten-free baking powder
200g pitted dates
1 tbsp honey
1 tbsp grated orange rind
1 tbsp biodynamic yoghurt
2 tbsp black tahini
½ cup pecans
½ cup olive oil
2 eggs
1 tsp stevia powder
1 tsp cinnamon
1 pinch sea salt

Pre-soak the quinoa in purified water for at least one hour. Then throw your dates into a saucepan, cover with boiling water and crank the heat up to high. Allow to boil for around 10 minutes. Stir and mash until the water has reduced and the dates have started to become very mushy, thick and stringy. Set aside to cool. In a large mixing bowl sift through flour and baking powder, and add the hazelnut meal and strained quinoa. Thoroughly combine. Crack in the eggs, the cooled date mixture, olive oil, tahini, pecans, yoghurt, cinnamon, honey, orange rind, stevia and salt. Thoroughly stir until the mixture is moist and well combined. If the mixture is too runny add a little more hazelnut meal. If the mixture is to dry, simply add a little more oil or yoghurt. You can't really screw this up; it would taste amazing raw. Using a little olive oil grease a slightly deep baking tray or cake tin and turn the mixture into this. Place in the oven at 180°C. After 10 minutes cover with foil, turn the heat down to 160°C and bake for a further 25 minutes. Do the old stick a knife in the middle of your loaf. If it comes out doughy, pop back in the oven for a bit longer. No worries.

AWESOME WITH

A hot sauce and vanilla ice cream. In a frypan add a little olive oil, the juice of the left over whole orange and a tablespoon of maple syrup. Bring to boil before pouring over a large piece of date loaf and add a scoop of vegan vanilla-bean ice cream.

ATMOSPHERE
Date loaf is a fabulous loaf to make in the autumn and winter months. Create for the whole family as a special healthy treat at anytime of the day. Enjoy snuggling up with a good movie, burn mandarin and cedar wood oils for calm and inner contentment, and appreciate the simple pleasures of life. Slice up your loaf and keep it covered in the fridge. It will keep for two or three working days. Hehehe..

STICKY

Serves 4

The journey must be one of discovery and observation. Participate in a culture rather than judge it."

Sticky rice is a simple and delicious dessert that is popular all over South-East Asia. I first tried black sticky rice in Thailand, and nearly cried it tasted so good. Mangos are a classic summer fruit. They are high in iron and vitamin C, making them awesome for our skin, bones and blood vessels. If mangos are not in season when you make your sticky rice, use bananas or lychees instead. Lemongrass pure essential oil when ingested helps to treat digestive disorders and fight infections.

2 cups sticky (glutinous) black rice
1 large can organic coconut milk
½ tsp ground sea salt
2 tbsp palm sugar
1 drop lemongrass pure essential oil
1 large ripe mango
2 tbsp coconut cream
1 handful mint leaves

Soak the black rice for one hour before you begin cooking. Combine the rice, coconut milk, salt and sugar in an uncovered saucepan with 1¼ cups of water. Stir and bring to boil over a moderate heat. Simmer the rice, stirring regularly, for about 25 minutes, or until all the liquid is absorbed. Thoroughly stir in one drop of lemongrass pure essential oil. Remove from the heat, cover the pan, and leave it to cool down for around five minutes.

AWESOME WITH
Spoon the hot sticky rice into dessert bowls, arrange sliced mango around it, and then drizzle cold coconut cream. Garnish with a sprinkle of palm sugar and mint leaves. As an alternative serving suggestion, firmly press the warm rice evenly into a tray lined with cooking paper, and garnish with a little more shaved palm sugar. Refrigerate until cold, then cut into diamond-shaped pieces.

TROPICAL FRUIT PIE

Serves 2

"If we didn't have cloudy days, we would never fully appreciate the sunshine."

Sweet and sensational! A deliciously fantastic summer dessert that won't ruin your waistline. The tropical fruit pie is a synergy of sweetness that supplies the body with energy, vitamins and minerals, and is rich in cell-repairing healthy fats and oils.

THE BASE
½ cup almond meal
6 organic fresh dates
100g organic raw cashews
1 tbsp shredded coconut
2 tbsp organic nut butter – Brazil, almond and cashew butter is best

THE TOPPING
1 red papaya
½ pineapple
2 lady finger bananas
1 tsp agave syrup
1 tbsp shredded coconut
1 tbsp slithered almonds
1 tbsp organic nut butter

Remove the seeds from the dates and begin by blending all the base ingredients in a food processor for two minutes. Refrigerate the base mix for one hour until the texture is dense and moist, allowing you to create two perfectly round medium-sized, semi-flattened piles onto two small separate plates (a base for each person). These piles are now the foundation for you to start building your tower of sweetness.

Begin the topping by thinly slicing up all the fresh fruits and placing the first layer of papaya on both bases, followed by a second layer of pineapple, then the banana slices. Drizzle your fruit tower with agave syrup and nut butter, then decorate with shredded coconut and slithered almonds. Finish off each tropical fruit pie with a fresh mint leaf and a good squeeze of lime.

ATMOSPHERE
Happy, happy, joy, joy! This is the kind of thing you eat with a smile across your face from start to finish. Enjoy with a special friend some-where in the sunshine, burn lemon and jasmine pure essential oils to empha-sise the importance of enjoying the delightful bliss in your life. Remember, there is nothing wrong with being lavish sometimes.

VEGAN DREAM

"Manifest your desires and allow your dreams to become your reality."

Vegans dream of delicious dairy-free alternatives to yoghurt, cream and cheese. Cashew nuts and firm tofu are both good alternatives to recreating dishes that require a cheese substitute. Coconut cream and its milk are a great alternative to yoghurt, ice cream and thickened cream.

COCONUT YOGHURT

1 can coconut cream
2 vanilla pods

Slice open the vanilla pods and scrape out the vanilla into a bowl filled with coconut cream. Then gently mix the delicate dark brown vanilla pod trail through the heavenly white creamery. Keep refrigerated in an airtight container for three days, enjoy with morning fruit, muesli and apple crumble.

LEMON SCENTED CREAM

1 can coconut cream
1 tsp grated lemon rind
½ tsp honey

In a small bowl thoroughly mix all the ingredients together and refrigerate for at least one hour until the cream is really cold. The lemon scented cream will keep refrigerated for three days and is delightful when dolloped on top of lemon scented scones, sponge and cheese cakes.

LEMONY CREAM CHEESE

1 cup raw macadamias
2 tbsp lemon juice
2 tbsp coconut cream
¼ tsp Celtic salt

In a food processor or blender, process all the ingredients together for two minutes or until smooth. Keep refrigerated in an airtight container for two weeks. Enjoy on warm toasted breads and scones with home-made jam, or use as a dip for crackers and fresh vegetables.

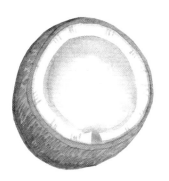

WINTER FRUIT CRUMBLE

Serves 6

"If you're not hungry cooking will create hunger. Cooking should tease, tempt and inspire you. Yes. It is a great art."

With its richness and warmth, this fragrant and wholehearted dessert makes you almost feel like skipping dinner… Abundant in dietary fibre, immunity-strengthening and circulation-pumping ingredients, the winter fruit crumble is a truly grand dessert for a chilly Sunday night to kick start you for a week of winter work.

1 organic peach
2 organic apricots
2 large Beurre Bosc pears
6 fresh organic dates
6 sulphate free dried apricots
½ cup sultanas
¼ cup marsala
2 tbsp raw yellow box honey
1 tsp cinnamon
1 tsp nutmeg
3 star aniseeds
2 whole cloves

THE CRUMBLE
2 cups old fashioned oats
1 cup sifted spelt flour
100g goat curd
1 pinch salt
2 tbsp tahini
½ cup apricot kernel oil

Start this winter sensation by washing and chopping all the fresh fruits into medium sized chunks; don't forget to remove all the seeds from the fruits. Thinly slice the dried dates and dried apricots. In a medium sized saucepan add two cups of water and bring to a fairly high heat; add all the fresh and dried fruits. After five minutes add the marsala, cinnamon, nutmeg, honey, aniseed and cloves. Stir. Once the fruity spicy goodness mix has reached boiling point, remove from the heat immediately and set aside to cool.

In a large glass bowl unite all the dry and wet crumble ingredients, making sure you mix them together exceptionally well (you may need to use your fingers to combine them successfully). Ensure the crumble mixture is moist and even in consistency. Spoon half of this mix into a small greased shallow baking tray and flatten out using your hands, pressing the ingredients firmly into the tray. Preheat the oven to 180°C. Now spread out the cooled fruit combination evenly upon the crumble base. Finish by scattering the second part of the crumble mixture over the top of the fruit layer. Place in the oven and cook for half an hour or until steamy and slightly golden. Remove and immediately serve into dessert bowls. Enjoy with the tofu whipped cream, yoghurt, custard or soy ice cream and an extra dusting of nutmeg.

TOFU WHIPPED CREAM
1 packet organic silken tofu
3 tbsp maple syrup
1 drop orange essential oil
1–2 tbsp almond or cashew butter

Place the ingredients into a blender or food processor for 30 seconds to a minute. Refrigerate and serve cold.

ATMOSPHERE

Sundays can be miraculous or kind of depressing. Some of us get the Sunday blues and dread this day of the week, as what follows is another week of banality. The weekends should be for nurturing, indulgence and fun! If you've got nothing else to do, make a habit of cooking your favourite meal, hiring out your favourite childhood movies and spending the day pampering yourself, eating good food and having a laugh. Enjoy your winter crumble dessert anytime on a Sunday, anywhere that is warm and comfortable. Prior to sleep, burn cedar wood, frankincense and cinnamon pure essential oils for reassurance and deep inner peace, because all is well!

ACCOMPANIMENTS

Often a side dish or sauce will perfectly complete a meal, adding extra flavour and nutritional benefits to a breakfast, lunch or dinner. Pretty much all of the following creations are made by hand, using a teaspoon of this and a dash of that. The recommended method when making all the accompaniments is to stir or blend the listed ingredients thoroughly together and serve in little attractive ceramic side dishes alongside any meals you think they would go well with.

BALI BUDDHA SAUCE

4 tbsp cashew butter
2 tbsp coconut cream
1 tsp chilli paste,
1 pinch salt
1 pinch cracked pepper
¼ cup fresh lime

To die for over brown rice and steamed vegetables, oven baked crunchy vegetables, or used as a marinade for red meat or chicken.

ARIGATO GOZAIMASU

2 tbsp umeboshi plum paste or sauce
2 tbsp tamari soy sauce
1 tsp minced parsley
½ tsp grated Spanish onion
1 tsp honey and 1 tsp sesame oil

This is a grand addition to Japanese food and various rice and fish dishes.

REAL SEAFOOD SAUCE

4 tbsp 100 per cent natural mayonnaise
1 tsp organic tomato paste
1 tsp fish sauce
1 tbsp fresh lime juice
1 tsp chilli paste

Sensational with home-made fish and chips and chunky potato wedges.

TOFU DOUBLE CREAM

1 packet organic silken tofu,
3 tbsp maple syrup
1 tsp vanilla extract
2 tbsp almond or cashew butter

Combine all the ingredients into a blender or food processor for one minute. Awesome with hot sticky date pudding, or alongside your favourite piece of cake.

THE MIDDLE EAST

2 tbsp hulled tahini
¼ cup fresh lemon
¼ cup extra virgin olive oil
1 tsp dill tips

Perfect with fish, meat, salads, steamed vegetables and bread. Just get this yummy spread onto something for goodness sake.

LEBANON

2 tbsp hummus
2 tbsp goat yoghurt
1 tsp ground pepper
¼ cup fresh lemon juice

Use as a dip for falafels, roasted sweet potato chips, fresh carrot and celery sticks.

GRECIAN GODDESS

4 tbsp goat yoghurt
½ cup grated cucumber
a few sultanas
a little thinly sliced Spanish onion
1 tsp paprika
1 tbsp lemon juice

This little bowl of creamy freshness goes well with Greek and Lebanese foods, or can be served simply with some pita or thin rice bread.

TART SAUCE

2 tbsp tahini
¼ cup 100 per cent natural balsamic vinegar
¼ cup fresh lemon juice
¼ cup extra virgin olive oil
½ tsp ground black pepper

This magic little mixture will keep refrigerated for two weeks and is a lovely dressing on salads and oven roasted vegetables.

ZESTY RELISH

4 tbsp date paste
squeeze lime juice
1 tbsp coconut oil

Interesting, sweet and tangy; add a dollop of this pleasant tasting paste to vegetable stir-fries, rice dishes, Thai, Malaysian and Indian food.

MINT CAFÉ COPYRIGHT – AKA HOT CINNAMON PRUNES IN SHEEP'S YOGHURT

1 small tub natural yoghurt
6 pitted prunes
½ cup water
1 tsp cinnamon powder

For two to three minutes pan fry a few large pitted prunes in a little water and one teaspoon of ground cinnamon. Place the hot prunes into a bowl of cold yoghurt and serve with pudding, muesli, oats or poached fruit. Absolute bliss!

FAT CAT

1 tbsp cashew butter
2 tbsp coconut cream
1 tsp cocoa powder
2 drops vanilla essence

Creamy, sweet and wholesome, a delicious accompaniment to pancakes, fresh fruits and ice cream.

PENIS BUTTER

4 tbsp organic crunchy peanut butter
2 tsp tamari soy sauce
¼ cup boiling water
1 squeeze lemon juice
½ tsp cayenne pepper

Penis butter is phenomenally delicious poured over roasted vegetables, eggs, chicken satay, fried tempeh and tofu stir-fry. Best served immediately whilst warm and runny.

MY MUM'S MARINADE

2 tbsp 100 per cent natural strawberry jam
1 tbsp olive oil
3 tbsp tamari soy sauce
dash red wine
dried thyme
rosemary

A fabulous pre-meat marinade for bar-bequed steaks, tofu and gourmet sausages.

TAHINI MISO

½ cup hulled tahini paste
1 tsp miso paste

Thoroughly mix together and this little bowl of salty, creamy awesomeness can be used to dress salads and roasted vegetables.

LEBANESE LOVE

1 tbsp extra virgin olive oil
1 tbsp lime juice
½ cup pomegranate juice
1 pinch salt and pepper

Mix together and drizzle over fresh salads, vine leaf or cabbage rolls, then garnish with fresh mint leaves.

SOUL CAKE SYRUP

6 pitted finely chopped dates
1 cup cherry juice
1 tbsp palm sugar
1 tsp ground cinnamon

Heat the ingredients in a saucepan for 15 minutes and pour this warm sauce on the top of sponge cakes and muffins to make them warm, moist and inviting.

ALICE IN WONDERLAND

4 tbsp tofu cream cheese
¼ cup fresh lemon juice
1 drop sweet orange essential oil
1 tsp rapadura sugar

Wonderful when added to warm orange and poppy seed muffins. Try pasting it on the base of a home-made oat or Anzac biscuit, and pressing it against another biscuit creating a lemony cream cheese biscuit sandwich treat!

GILI SPRINKLE

Equal parts:
goji berries
linseeds
roasted buckwheat
raw sunflower
pumpkin seeds

Thoroughly mix together and keep in an airtight container. Sprinkle on fresh fruit salad, porridge and yoghurt for an antioxidant and protein boost.

SUNSHINE SPRINKLE

Equal amounts:
ground sea salt
ground black pepper
turmeric powder
celery powder
sesame seeds
a small handful raw rice grains

Add to a salt shaker and use in curries, rice pilaffs, laksa, scrambled eggs, roasted vegetables and soups. The sunshine sprinkle adds colour, taste and extra nutritional benefits.

CHAPTER FOUR

DRINK RECIPES

Organic fruits and vegetables have far more nutritional value and cleanliness than produce treated with pesticides, therefore it is better to make beverages using organic ingredients. It is also compulsory to use certified organic soy and dairy products in all your creations."

ANTI-CANCER DRINK

Serves 1

"The best doctors and nutritionists in the world are ourselves."

In Asia, turmeric (curcuma longa) is well recognised as the best antioxidant, hypoglycaemic, colorant, antiseptic and wound healer around. The active ingredient in turmeric is curcumin, which makes it one of nature's most powerful healers. For thousands of years in India, turmeric has been used for its anti-inflammatory effects and many health benefits.

The medicinal properties of this spice still continue to be revealed. It is known for its miraculous power in the treatment of tumours, cancer and melanoma. Drink this beverage daily as an illness preventative. Many traditional healers will tell you that if you are sick you need to consume the turmeric drink every day for three months.

2 cm grated turmeric root
1 glass room temperature purified water
1 lime wedge
1 tsp raw honey

Grate up the turmeric root into a glass; add the honey, lime and water. Stir well, and drink 15 minutes before eating twice per day. The mother root of fresh turmeric is the most effective part of the turmeric root.

COMPLETE THERAPY

Serves 1

"Read the directions, even if you don't follow them."

This refreshing and delightful drink will infuse your body with a variety of enzymes and good bacteria, leaving you feeling cleansed and energised. Drink every day, preferably first thing in the morning 30 minutes before food, for maximum absorption and effect. Kombucha is not just a health tonic; it is a complete therapy that helps with long-term illnesses such as arthritis, digestive disorders, high blood pressure, kidney illness, poor circulation, high cholesterol and cancer. Kombuchi tea combined with noni, pineapple and coconut juice provides the vitamins and minerals your body requires for maximum health and wellbeing.

100ml cold kombucha tea
30ml Tahitian noni juice
50ml fresh pineapple juice
50ml fresh coconut water
2 ice cubes

Pour all the ingredients into a chilled glass, add two ice cubes and gently stir. If you are catering for more than one person adjust this recipe accordingly.

ЯE YOUR COLD AND
J TEA

Serves 1

"Emotion always has its roots in the unconscious and manifests itself in the body."

In order to fight off and prevent the onset of any kind of infection or virus the human body needs to be loaded with immunity-boosting herbs, vitamins and minerals. This provides the body with the strength to be less affected by disease. When the immune system is strong, well fed, rested and warm it can't help but heal and repair more effectively. Rosehips are high in vitamin C, which is very healing; honey has antibacterial properties; apple cider vinegar and lemon help maintain the correct pH balance in the body; while ginger is a natural antibiotic which is nice and warming when you're sick.

1 tsp rosehips
1 tsp raw honey
1 tsp apple cider vinegar
2 cm grated ginger
2 cm grated turmeric
2 slices lemon
1 cup boiling water
A splash of cold water

Place all the dry and damp ingredients into a teapot or plunger and splash cold water over them, so when you add boiling water, the ingredients are not shocked and the medicinal properties are not damaged. Add the boiling water and give the concoction about ten to twelve minutes brewing time. Drink three times per day for the best results.

ATMOSPHERE

This tea needs to be drunk somewhere warm, under a blanket in a comfortable space where you feel relaxed. A hot water bottle or wheat pack should be placed across the upper back, as it allows the body to heal faster. A hot bath of Epsom salts is recommended, as this will help remove toxicity from the joints especially if the cold or flu is viral. Steam or burn pure essential oils of eucalyptus for congestion, lavender to calm the respiratory system, and thyme for its warming effect.

EARL GREY

"I act with honour, respect and dignity; I respect others and myself."

Make your own Earl Grey tea by combining the smooth yet aromatic flavours of a good quality fine black tea with a beautifully bitter bergamot, resulting in a medium-bodied, fruity, bold blend. Pure bergamot essential oil has a stimulating effect that increases secretion of digestive juices, bile and insulin, aiding digestion and the proper absorption of nutrients. Black tea contains antioxidants, which protect us from disease.

1 medium sized paper bag
200g organic loose leaf black tea
2 drops 100 per cent pure bergamot oil
200g glass airtight jar

Combine all the above ingredients into a paper bag and gently shake it about. Leave the mix sealed in the paper bag for one night, before storing in the airtight glass jar. Brew a tablespoon in a teapot and enjoy at breakfast time outside in the sunshine.

GINGER CORDIAL

"Body and soul cannot be separated for purposes of treatment, for they are one and indivisible. In order to heal our bodies, we must heal our minds."

Many historical writings will refer to ginger as both a spiritual and a heavenly herb. Ginger has been used since the beginning of time for optimum digestive health.

8 cups boiling water
1 large organic ginger root
2 limes
4 whole cloves
2 tbsp agave nectar
1 bunch fresh mint

In a large saucepan, bring water to a boil. Thinly grate the ginger and finely slice the limes.

Place the ginger, limes and whole cloves in the boiling water for two minutes. Turn off the stove and thoroughly stir in the agave nectar. Allow to cool, and cover. Leave the concoction to ferment for 24 hours. Strain the liquid into a glass bottle and refrigerate until you're ready to drink.

Add the ginger cordial to gin, tequila or your favourite spirit. Top up with mineral water, add some crushed ice and garnish with sliced lime and mint. The piss head free alternative would be to ditch the alcohol and enjoy with chilled or sparkling water and ice.

I HEART BLUEBERRIES

Serves 2

"You don't have to always play it safe; the hands of the universe will always be there to catch you when you fall."

All berries are awesome, but out of all the berries, blueberries hold some of the best antioxidant awesomeness. These antioxidants keep your body profoundly healthy, preventing and even reversing chronic disease. Blueberries have also been found to contain resveratrol, a potential anti-cancer agent, and the antioxidants in blueberries neutralize DNA-damaging free radicals, reducing cell damage. The Native Americans called them star berries, because the five points of blueberry blossom make a star shape, confirming their true superstar health benefits. This blueberry smoothie tastes excellent, and is one of the easiest ways to get a whole lot of nutrients in one meal.

1 punnet organic blueberries
800ml non-GM organic soy milk
2 tbsp sheep's yoghurt
1 tbsp goji berries
1 tsp coconut oil
1 tsp LSA
1 tsp raw honey
1 tsp cinnamon

Lovingly place all the ingredients into a blender and blend for 30 seconds to a minute. Pour into chilled glasses and enjoy in the morning as a light breakfast or mid morning snack. This smoothie is wonderfully abundant in essential nutrients – try making the blueberry smoothie every day for a week; by Thursday you will be bouncing off the walls!

KIDNEY FRIENDLY PROTEIN SHAKE

Serves 1

"When we encourage others, we fill their hearts with courage."

Nature always provides us with everything we require. In order to build muscle tissue and repair cell damage the body needs a sufficient supply of protein. Synthetic protein powders have gained popularity in recent years due to the convenience for those with high exercise and weight training agendas. However, synthetic protein and whey powders are not natural and can put strain on the body and damage to kidneys.

What do you get when you consume a shake that combines complete protein with potassium, magnesium, selenium and antioxidants? The most energy filled, physically abundant day of your life. Make this delicious 100 per cent natural shake pre- and post-workout as often as required. Understand that managing your health isn't always as convenient as spooning powder into a cup. All the best things in life require effort, and your body is worth the effort.

2 cups almond milk
1 tbsp LSA
1 tbsp almond oil
1 biodynamic egg
1 tbsp cashew butter
1 banana
¼ cup raw cocoa nibs
1 tsp ground nutmeg

Combine all ingredients into a blender or milkshake maker and blend for one to two minutes until smooth. Pour into a glass, dust with a little nutmeg, and enjoy nourishing your body with some of the most cell loving, tissue building, and muscle repairing natural ingredients you will ever encounter.

MY CHAI

Serves 4

*"My wish is to serve humanity;
I am dedicated to helping others."*

Chai originally comes from India. It is made with compatible herbs and spices that are known for their medicinal properties. Today, Chai is enjoyed for its unique spicy flavour all over the world. There is nothing more disheartening than ordering a chai latte in a café and being served a weak and inauthentic version of rubbish. My chai has depth, soul, a hint of delicate honey sweetness and is incredibly warming. You can drink chai hot or cold. Chai tea is also absolutely amazing when used in place of water when cooking porridge.

4 cups water
4 cups soy milk
2 cloves
2 black peppercorns
2 green cardamom pods
2 cinnamon sticks
2 tsp ground cinnamon powder
3 tbsp Earl Grey loose leaf tea
2 tbsp dandelion loose leaf tea
2cm grated fresh ginger root
3 tbsp honey

Place all the herbs, spices and tea into a medium sized saucepan. Cover the ingredients with boiling water and stir. Allow the mixture to sit for a few hours on a very low heat, adding more water as the herbs begin to dry up. When you are almost ready to drink it, add the soy milk and honey, turn up the heat and bring to boil. Turn down the heat again and simmer for 25 minutes before serving. To make a strong chai tea, brewing time is generally a few hours, but you can simmer for longer if you like. You can drink chai tea throughout the day, ladling from the saucepan into cups, just like they do on the streets of India where they serve from big clay pots for all to enjoy.

OKRA – DIABETIC DRINK

Serves 1

"If there are stars in the night sky you know the following day will be sunny."

Having okra on a daily basis is very good if you are suffering from the symptoms of diabetes. Okra has properties that help your body metabolize glucose and stabilise blood sugar levels. It's worthwhile mentioning that the okra drink is beneficial for soothing an inflamed stomach and digestive system.

1 cup purified water
1 okra

Wash the okra, cut off the two ends, and slice it down the middle. Then place the okra in a cup of purified water, cover and allow to sit over night. In the morning remove the okra from the cup, and drink the remaining water turned slimy juice on an empty stomach. Wait for around 30 minutes before eating or drinking anything else. According to the proponents of this cure, your diabetes will soon be much better, if not completely cured.

RAZOR BLADES

"I always speak from the heart. What I have to say is worthy of being heard."

This sore throat tincture is a highly effective remedy that will rapidly numb and cure an incredibly sore throat. The chosen ingredients have traditionally been used in natural therapies to efficiently alleviate viral infections and banish illness from the body. One of the major components of the volatile oils present in cloves greatly serves a tender throat by acting as an anti-inflammatory, antifungal and analgesic. This multiple clove action becomes highly successful when combined with fresh lime juice rich in vitamin C, manuka honey which is soothing and healing, and pure coconut oil, which treats viral infections and protects cell membranes.

6 whole clove buds
4 tbsp organic pure coconut oil
1 tbsp manuka honey
1 lime

In a small ceramic dish add the cloves, coconut oil and honey. Squeeze in the lime and stir thoroughly as the lime juice emulsifies the coconut oil and honey. Cover and allow the mixture to sit for at least an hour to allow for the tincture to extract the medicinal properties of the clove buds. Swallow a teaspoon of the syrup every two hours. Sucking on the cloves is recommended for further numbing and healing the throat.

STICKY DATE DRINK

Serves 2

"There is no such thing as failure. Life is about learning the lessons you require for spiritual and emotional growth."

This is a deliciously sweet and fantastically healthy drink. Dates contain a variety of B-complex vitamins – thiamine, riboflavin, niacin and vitamin B6. These vitamins have a range of functions that help to metabolize carbohydrates, sustain blood glucose levels and maintain a healthy body. Almond milk contains B vitamins in the form of riboflavin, plus other muscle regulating nutrients like iron. The combination of dates and almonds, plus the circulatory stimulating benefits of pure essential orange oil and cinnamon, makes the sticky date drink an impressive option for any time of the day.

3 cups almond milk
3 fresh dates
1 tsp raw honey
½ tsp ground cinnamon powder
½ tsp nutmeg
1 drop orange pure essential oil

Blend all the ingredients together for one minute. Serve cold with ice, or add to a saucepan and heat for a few minutes to serve warm in the colder months. The sticky date drink goes profoundly well with a piece of sticky date pudding, a good book and the sweet lingering notes of orange and ginger pure essential oils fragrantly disseminating throughout the home. Moments like this bring peace and happiness.

SWEET BASIL SLUSHY

Serves 6

"Herbs bring out the potential in an individual."

Enjoy this herbaceous drink when you're feeling in the mood for something or someone exotic! Basil has a complex, sweet, spicy aroma that offers unique compounds containing powerful elements proven to enhance circulation, stabilise blood sugar levels and improve respiratory issues.

½ cup coconut sugar
¼ cup basil leaves
250ml water
1 cup gin
½ cup fresh lime juice
6 lychees
1L mineral water
1 cup crushed ice

Gently simmer the coconut sugar, basil leaves and water in a saucepan for five minutes. Allow it to cool, before placing in a blender, and blending for two minutes. Strain the mixture through a sieve into a jug along with the gin, lime juice, lychees, mineral water and crushed ice. Serve the slushies in chilled margarita-style cocktail glasses, and enjoy morning, noon or night!

THE ACAI BERRY BOYS

"Optimum nutrition is a one way street to optimum health."

The Acai Berry Boys drink is a steaming hot cup of spicy and decadent deliciousness! Chocolate begins with a bean... and ends with a smile! This hot chocolate-style beverage is not for the faint-hearted, a few cups and you're utterly off your face... off your face on antioxidant and aphrodisiac ingredients that completely cheer the soul and restore the spirit. Be careful as you may just find yourself pashing off in a dark corner with someone you have suddenly fallen in love with. Cacao is remarkably rich in sulphur and magnesium; this is one of the reasons women crave chocolate during the menstrual period. Magnesium balances brain chemistry, hormones and builds strong bones. Raw cacao is high in the beauty mineral sulphur. Sulphur builds strong nails, strong hair, shiny skin, detoxifies the liver, and supports healthy pancreas function.

500g ground raw cocoa beans
1L coconut milk
2.5L purified water
100g block dark chocolate
1 cup carob powder
1 tbsp stevia powder
2 tbsp maca powder
2 tbsp shaved coconut flakes
½ cup goji berries
½ cup acai berries
1 tsp ground cinnamon
1 tsp ground nutmeg
1 tsp ground cloves
1 tsp ground chilli powder
A pinch Himalayan rock salt

Warning – This recipe serves 10 people. Reduce all the ingredients accordingly if you are catering for a smaller crew.

Place the water, coconut milk and ground cocoa beans into a large deep saucepan and heat at medium temperature. Stir continuously allowing the powder and liquid to combine. Then add all the other precious ingredients. There is no need to break up the block of chocolate, just throw it in and allow it to melt and marinate in this pot of decadence. Bring everything to boil for two minutes, and immediately reduce to a low heat for one hour. Stir every 10 minutes. If the mixture becomes too thick, add more water.

ATMOSPHERE
Wait for a chilly night to brew up a batch of this hot chocolate. Invite over a few crazy people for a midweek game night or movie marathon. Deck out your lounge room with lamps, candles, comfy blankets bean bags and cushions. Dedicate a table to the centre of the room and place the pot of hot chocolate so high on a pedestal that you have to climb up to serve it. Burn a blend of bergamot, rose and ginger essential oils, allowing your guests to feel complete joy and love in their hearts.

TROPICAL VEGAN SMOOTHIE

Serves 2

*"I accept and value myself just
as I am; I choose how to think
and behave."*

This tropical cocktail of wholefoods keeps you energised and vibrant. It is completely chockers with enzymes and vitamins and minerals important for immunity and restoration. The primary therapeutic benefit of papaya is derived from its enzyme, papain, a powerful digestive aid that helps the stomach to break down protein and facilitate the absorption of nutrients.

1 cup chopped papaya
1 cup chopped pineapple
3 cups coconut water
2 ice cubes
1 pinch ground sea salt
1 tsp raw honey

Blend all the ingredients together for two minutes and serve in chilled glasses on a hot summer's afternoon; Garnish with a mint leaf and umbrella straw. If you feel the need, add a shot of vodka or coconut liqueur before blending.

DOCTOR JUICE

"Never be in a hurry, do everything quietly and in a calm spirit. Do not lose your inner peace for anything whatsoever.

These days we all know daily juicing is the go! It's the go for weight loss, detoxification and alkalizing the body, and is the key to abundant health and vitality. Fruit and vegetable juices work on a cellular level and purify the blood. They cast out the toxic elements accumulated in the cells of the body, and help to nourish, replenish and beautify your being.

SKINNY JUICE
DRINK ME FOR:
Poor Metabolism, Sluggishness, Fluid Retention, Congestion, Fatigue, Metabolic Disorders and Bloating

INGREDIENTS:
1 cup of purified water
The juice of 1 grapefruit
2 green apples
1 cup of chopped pineapple
The juice of half a lemon
1 teaspoon of grated ginger
Small pinch of cayenne pepper
2mls of green tea extract
1 teaspoon of chia seeds.

DETOX JUICE
DRINK ME FOR:
All Skin Conditions, Poor metabolism, Lethargy, Congestion, Liver Cleanse, Candida, Fluid Retention and Bloating

INGREDIENTS:
1 cup purified water
2 beetroots
2 purple carrots
1 cup of spinach
The juice of half a lime
1 teaspoon of grated turmeric root
5ml of both dandelion and St Mary's Thistle liquid extract.

SKIN THERAPY JUICE
DRINK ME FOR:
Acne, Acne Rosacea, Flawless Skin Tone, Anti-Ageing, Eczema, Pigmentation, Psoriasis, Dry, Red and Irritated skin

INGREDIENTS:
1 cup of coconut water
2 carrots
1 cup of chopped papaya
1/2 a cup of blueberries
1 teaspoon raw honey
5ml noni juice concentrate
The juice of half a lime
Small pinch of Himalayan rock salt
5ml of both gotu kola liquid extract
silica liquid extract.

CHAPTER FIVE

BATH RECIPES

"The ancient tradition of bathing is a marvellous experience. Add the finest and purest ingredients to your bath to cleanse and heal your being. All essential oils you use must be extracted from 100 per cent natural and organic sources."

BATHING TIPS

"Clarity is bound to come to those who seek."

Epsom salt baths are highly therapeutic. Adding pure essential oils and clays to an Epsom salt bath is beneficial for cleansing the skin and alleviating muscle pain and fluid retention.

Dry skin brushing is highly stimulating for the lymphatic system and exfoliates the skin, encouraging new cell formation. It also increases blood circulation, which promotes detoxification.

Cold water rinse should always conclude a bath or shower. This closes the skin's pores, increases circulation and leaves you feeling revitalised.

Hydrate before and after bathing with herbal teas and purified water.

Moisturise your damp skin from head to toe with a natural good quality body oil and rich body cream after a shower or bath.

Natural bath and shower products that are free from synthetic ingredients and petrochemicals are the best to use as they are good for your health and the environment.

For dry and damaged skin, bathe in almond, olive and apricot kernel oils. Use coconut and goat's milk products to cleanse. Add pure essential oils of rose, patchouli and sandalwood to your bath to replenish dehydrated skin.

For oily and acne-prone skin, add green clay, magnesium and witch hazel or apple cider vinegar to your bath. Choose juniper berry, lavender, tea tree, lime, lemon, petitgrain, mandarin and geranium pure essential oils to cleanse away impurities and balance the sebaceous glands.

For burns, eczema, psoriasis and extremely sensitive skin, bathe in a lukewarm bath containing goat's milk, manuka honey, coconut oil, oats and loose leaf chamomile and lavender flowers.

CLEOPATRA'S BATH

"Dissolve away in this decadent bathing experience that is inspired by the spectacular love story of the Egyptian queen, Cleopatra."

To recreate a bath named after Queen Cleopatra is not a cliché, it's a classic! The timeless goddess was famous for her beautiful skin, the consequence of bathing in milk, flowers and essential oils. There is something mysteriously feminine about Cleopatra. It is inspiring when a woman is in touch with her sexuality. Coconut milk is very nourishing, and the rose oils are incredibly hydrating. The combination makes a repairing and soothing remedy for dry and irritated skin. Pink clay is very toning, leaving your skin soft and supple. Cleopatra used balms and scents as part of her pre-love making preparation. There were clearly no sacral chakra blockages for this lady.

YOU WILL NEED
1 tbsp pink clay
20ml coconut milk
1 handful dry or fresh rose petals
2 drops rose otto or rose absolute pure essential oil

ATMOSPHERE
This bath recipe is best enjoyed in the evening hours in a quiet and empty house. Feel free to light candles and burn neroli, palmarosa and geranium essential oils for their balancing, comforting and nurturing properties. Have a large white fluffy towel and a pot of white rose petal tea awaiting your bathing departure. Any type of Middle Eastern music will contribute to the exotic ambience. Fill the bath with warm water, add pink clay, coconut milk, the rose pure essential oils and rose petals. Bless your bath with thoughts of femininity, strength and success – all the things Cleopatra represents.

ENLIGHTENMENT BATH

"Agnostics believe absolute religious truth can be known, but is only revealed to enlightened humans."

Everyone needs a little magic in their life, a sacred ceremony that unites you with your higher self. The Enlightenment Bath is a blissful bathing experience that supports spiritual clarity by using a magical blend of frankincense, lavender and lime pure essential oils to dissolve your worries, heighten your senses and reconnect your spirit. The amethyst crystal is used to guard against guilt and fearful feelings, and develop spiritual wisdom.

You will need
1 amethyst crystal
1 purple candle
2 drops lavender pure essential oil
2 drops frankincense pure essential oil
2 drops lime pure essential oil
10ml bath dispersant

Atmosphere
This supernatural ceremony begins with a prayer – ask your god or your higher self for your highest guidance to come through. Fill your bath with water, add the pure essential oils, bath dispersant and amethyst. Dim the lights, play meditation music, light the candle and place it nearby. Slide into the calm waters and begin your bathing experience by taking five full breaths in through your nose and out through your mouth. Spend the rest of the bath time simply letting go of erratic thoughts and negative judgments. Visualise the colour gold around the top of your head. All you have is here and now, so surrender and just be.

FUYU – WINTER BATH

"Natural medicine is an integration of the mind, body and soul. Natural therapies bring out the potential in each individual."

Yuzu fruit is a type of citrus fruit that grows throughout Japan. It looks much like a small tangerine and has a distinctive zesty fragrance that is captivating. In Japan you can get bottled yuzu juice at the supermarket. I mix it with sake, soda and fresh mint. In Japan, it is a tradition to use the yuzu fruit and its juice in a hot bath on the day of the winter solstice known as Toji, to ward off a range of winter illnesses, such as colds and flu. Yuzu is very high in nutrients and antioxidants. Taking a yuzu bath is believed to bring you wealth and good health. When you bathe in pure essential oils they are absorbed through the skin and enter the bloodstream which has many beneficial effects including, strengthening the immunity and fighting off free radicals which accelerate ageing.

You will need
A hot bath
2 yuzu fruits or 3 drops pure yuzu essential oil
(Use lime, lemon or pure essential oils if you can't get any yuzu)
1 tbsp ground ginger powder
1 cup Epsom salts
2 white candles

Atmosphere
Squeeze the juice and flesh of the two yuzu fruits into your hot bath and throw in the other ingredients, including the leftover yuzu skin which holds the oil. Light two white candles to symbolise purity and unity between body and mind. Crank up the sounds of some old school Enya and sail away! Your shoulders and head should be above the water level, to enjoy the full warming effect from the bottom up. In an oil burner blend a few drops of lemon, orange and rosemary pure essential oils for energy and vitality. You'll emerge from your yuzu bath feeling light, refreshed and uplifted.

HARVEST MOON BATH AND BODY POLISH

"Embrace the flow of life and live in unity with the planet. There is no separation between humans and the universe."

This nourishing bath and body polish recipe was created to promote healthy, glowing skin by polishing away dead skin cells and cleansing away impurities using ingredients that leave your body soft and sparkling. Exfoliation works to improve circulation, stimulate new skin cell growth, and promote the body's natural secretion of oils, which relieves dry and flaky skin.

YOU WILL NEED
1 cup coconut oil
2 cups sea salt
3 drops ylang ylang pure essential oil
2 drops orange pure essential oil
2 drops lime pure essential oil
4 frangipani flowers
2 tea light candles

Combine sea salt, coconut oil and pure essential oils in a mixing bowl, so they can be rubbed onto the body.

Fill the bath a quarter of the way with warm water, add the flowers, light the candles and place the bowl of body polish mixture nearby. Enter the bath, slightly wet your skin and pick up handfuls of the polish and start rubbing it into the skin circular motions. Start at the feet and work your way up, paying special attention to the dry and rough areas. When you are satisfied that you are well and truly exfoliated, fill the bath with more warm water and relax in the tub for 10 minutes, allowing the exotic tropical aromas to awaken your senses.

After exfoliation always apply a moisturiser to keep your skin soft and hydrated. Sip on jasmine tea and slip into some silky pyjamas and enjoy your silky smooth skin. Although your outer being is not everything, it sure feels nice to feel nice.

NEW MOON

"New moons signify the completion or culmination of what may have been initiated during the previous month."

Astrology is based on the cycles of the planets and the interplay between them as they cruise around the solar system. A new moon, half moon or even a blue moon, are great times for reflection, cleansing and a celebration of new beginnings. Here is a new moon bath recipe that smells utterly enchanting. It helps clear stale energy, repels negative emotions, and leaves you feeling inspired about the future. Other things you can do to become enthusiastic about life are make a list of goals, spring clean your house, and discover a new hobby.

YOU WILL NEED
100g jar
100g Celtic rock salt
3 drops cypress essential oil
4 drops frankincense essential oil
2 tbsp extra virgin olive oil
1 small bunch fresh sage
1 quartz crystal

Using a sterilised spoon, combine the salts, olive oil and essentials oils in a glass bowl. It is important to ensure the ingredients are thoroughly combined before spooning into a clean, darkly coloured airtight jar; this ensures that the ingredients aren't compromised and the product will keep for a few months.

Bathe on the morning of a new moon or any time that represents a new beginning for you. Take a bath between the hours of 5am and 7am as the sun is rising. Throw in a heaped tablespoon of the new moon bath salts into warm water. Add a handful of the fresh sage and the quartz crystal, and ensure the bathroom is dark and candlelit. Drink at least two glasses of purified water after the new moon bath to assist detoxification. A yoga or meditation class to follow this bathing experience would ensure a meaningful start to the day.

THE ART OF BLENDING

"Art is about self expression. It is a way to run away without leaving home."

The blending of pure essential oils is somewhat like making music because aromas are composed of base, middle and top notes to deliver the perfect synergy of aroma and emotional effect. There are many ways pure essential oils can be used to promote a feeling of wellbeing – some of the best ways are by making your own bath, body and massage oils and using pure essential oils in an oil burner or diffuser.

Following are some delightful bath recipes. If you like you can add the pure essential oil blends to 25ml of a base oil like almond oil, to make a massage oil, or enjoy their aroma in an oil burner or vaporiser.

Best clarity blend – Gain a little insight
2 drops rosemary, 2 drops frankincense, 1 drop lemon
10ml bath dispersant

Best study blend – Focus to engage
3 drops rosemary, 2 drops lime, 1 drop basil
10ml bath dispersant

Best gentleman blend – Bring out the solid man in you
3 drops sandalwood, 2 drops orange, 2 drops patchouli
10ml bath dispersant

Best goddess blend – Unleash your inner femininity
2 drops jasmine, 2 drops ylang ylang, 1 drop ginger
10ml bath dispersant

Best depression blend – Dissolve away your sadness
2 drops rose, 2 drops bergamot, 2 drops cedarwood
10ml bath dispersant

Best exhaustion blend – Restore your spirit
2 drops vetiver, 2 drops peppermint, 3 drops lime
10ml bath dispersant

Best emotional intelligence blend – Listen to your higher self
2 drops petitgrain, 2 drops neroli, 2 drops frankincense
10ml bath dispersant

CHAPTER SIX

SKIN RECIPES

"It is preferred that when creating your own skincare products that you use pure essential oils, plant oils and other ingredients that are extracted from 100 per cent organic sources. Your skin, being your largest organ, will greatly appreciate the quality of the nourishing goodness you feed it."

AROMATHERAPY SKIN SAFETY RULES

- When using pure essential oils for vaporising, bathing, massage, soap making and skincare preparations make sure the oils come from a 100 per cent natural and reliable source; certified organic oils are best. You know organic essential oils are legitimate when they have a stamp of certification, botanical name and use-by date clearly printed on the label.

- When using pure essential oils in making your own skincare products, ensure you follow the correct dilution ratio depending on the individual or remedy purpose.

- Using pure essential oils in body care is a ratio of one to three per cent dilution for making creams, body oils, ointments and lotions for the body.

- Using pure essential oils in face care is a ratio of one quarter per cent dilution for making cleansers, oils and creams for the face.

- Using pure essential oils for babies is a ratio of one quarter to one half per cent dilution for making baby products. You are limited to using pure essential oils that are safe for infants such as lavender, mandarin and Roman chamomile.

- Using essential oils for pets is a ratio of one quarter per cent dilution for making shampoo and skincare products.

- Although essential oils are natural, they can be toxic if used in excess or incorrectly. Note that not all essential oils can be used in skincare, some oils are considered hazardous, and several pure essential oils may not be appropriate for everyone's health status and constitution. This is especially true if you are dealing with high blood pressure, epilepsy, cancer and diabetes.

- Always store pure essential oils and aromatherapy products in a cool environment, away from sunlight so the therapeutic properties are not compromised.

- Sun sensitivity, also known as phototoxicity, occurs when certain essential oils are used in skincare and cause the skin to be more sensitive to sunlight, making the skin burn and damage more easily. Avoid citrus oils like lime, lemon, bergamot, orange and mandarin if you are going to spend time in the sun.

- Pregnancy – Some essential oils should not be used if you are pregnant or lactating. Many aromatherapists consider it wise to avoid jasmine, rose, clary sage, peppermint, hyssop, rosemary, sage, basil, fennel, pennyroyal and nutmeg, especially in the first three months of pregnancy. Many pure essential oils are safe for pregnant women; However, consult an experienced aromatherapist before you use any oils to make sure you avoid uterine stimulation or possible toxicity. During pregnancy, always use a low dilution of pure essential oils.

- Never apply pure essential oils directly to the skin. Lavender (lavandula angustifolia) is the only exception to this rule.

- Less is more when using essential oils; large quantities of aromatherapy oils will only aggravate the skin. Your skin is your largest organ and what you put on it will be absorbed into the system, so take it easy with using essential oils too liberally.

BLACK MAGIC WOMAN

"The best way to find out if you can trust somebody is to trust them."

I put a spell on you and now you're mine! Cast a spell on that special somebody you truly desire by creating your very own aphrodisiac and confidence promoting oil that is bound to turn heads and melt hearts. Scents and aromas impact, trigger and manipulate our feelings. Another way to capture the heart of a potential lover is to be your authentic self, look them in the eye, tell them how you feel, and send the person your most loving and selfless energy.

25ml glass bottle
25ml jojoba oil
1 small rose quartz crystal
6 drops jasmine pure essential oil
4 drops ylang ylang pure essential oil
4 drops orange pure essential oil
3 drops cedarwood pure essential oil
2 drops ginger pure essential oil

Fill your glass bottle with the jojoba oil then carefully add all the pure essential oils. Conclude by adding the rose quartz crystal to infuse your creation with love and abundance. Gently shake your oil, hold the bottle in your hands, close your eyes and visualise someone you desire; imagine how it would feel to have them as a lover. Dab a little on your wrists, chest and the neck. Always label and date your products and store them in a cool dark environment.

CELEBRITY SKIN

"It's okay and even important to want something, but it's not okay to need something."

Like any organ, your skin requires several things to stay healthy: antioxidants, essential fatty acids, moisture and oxidation. If you lucked out genetically on having perfectly smooth, well nourished skin, do something about it. It may well require a smidgen of effort and consistency, but after all isn't our skin an important investment?

Very dry and damaged skin requires a daily oil and water phase for optimum nourishment and repair. Apply a 100 per cent organic cold pressed plant base oil of either coconut, olive, apricot, almond, avocado, sunflower, macadamia or grape seed oil to your entire body; if your skin is damp the moisture will help to emulsify the oil and absorb into the skin more easily. All plant oils are great, but you will need to determine which one your skin responds to best. Once the oil is absorbed, generously lavish your skin with a 100 per cent natural thick body cream. It is vital to seek out a product that contains shea, cocoa, vegetable glycerine, and other plant solids and waxes. Pure essential oils of sandalwood, patchouli, frankincense, geranium, everlasting, rose, palmarosa, jasmine, lavender and neroli are all fantastic for revitalising neglected skin. Remember not to be fooled into buying cheap body oils or creams that contain mineral oil, artificial fragrances and parabens because nutritionally these products do nothing for the skin. All legitimate products have a stamp of certification and meet the certified natural and organic standards.

ELIXIR OF IMMORTALITY

"Imagine the world if we only knew unconditional love: to give love and openly receive love."

One of the best ways to keep the skin young, healthy and strong is to use good quality pure organic plant oils. These oils are beneficial for their anti-ageing components, which promote cell renewal and rejuvenation so the skin stays supple, dewy and well fed. Create your own facial elixir using ingredients that are high in antioxidants, essential fatty acids and skin repairing and replenishing ingredients that feed your skin. Evening primrose oil contains essential fatty acids and linoleic acid, which promote cell growth and development. Apricot kernel oil is nourishing and revitalising to fine and sensitive skins. Frankincense, carrot seed and sandalwood pure essential oils encourage the growth of skin cells, improve skin tone and elasticity.

50ml glass bottle
25ml evening primrose oil
25ml apricot kernel oil
4 drops frankincense pure essential oil
2 drops carrot seed pure essential oil
2 drops sandalwood pure essential oil

Blend all the ingredients together in a sterilised glass bottle. Freely massage half a teaspoon into a clean damp face, neck and décolletage each evening. Facial massage is especially beneficial because it helps to stimulate blood circulation, relieve tension and prevent wrinkles. You will notice you sleep better when using this oil, as frankincense and sandalwood help to slow down the breath and encourage a more relaxed and peaceful state of mind.

GEISHA FACE

"Live your life how you like it."

Rice bran oil has been used by Japanese women for centuries to help achieve their legendary flawless complexions. In the west, uneven skin tone and blotchiness is a common disorder. The Geisha Face recipe is a gentle exfoliating treatment mask that promotes the growth of new skin cells, soothes redness and repairs cell damage. Rice flour, rice bran oil, cinnamon powder, rose water, almond oil and almond meal leave the skin silky smooth, glowing and beautiful, just like a Geisha!

1 tsp rice flour
1 tsp rice bran oil
1 tsp almond meal
1 tsp almond oil
¼ tsp cinnamon power
1 bottle 100 per cent natural rose water

Prepare a small clean bowl and teaspoon. Add the rice flour, rice bran oil and almond meal to the bowl. Slowly pour in a little rose water and stir. You are trying to achieve a smooth paste-like consistency so slowly adding the rose water is important. If the mixture seems too thick add a little more rose water. If it's all a little too runny, add a bit more rice flour. Gather the glorious paste in your hands and using circular motions, massage into a clean damp face, neck and décolletage for approximately three minutes. Leave the treatment to sit on the face for a further five minutes, then remove with warm water and a soft sponge.

HOT LEGS

"I once complained about having no shoes, until I met a man with no legs."

The trick to sexy pins is achieved through exercise. Yoga, walking, standing on your tippy toes and taking the stairs as often as possible are very effective ways to get lean calves and shrink, as my Aunty Lyn would say, those thunder thighs.

A little sun or spray tan will temporarily make any area look slimmer and more appealing. Exfoliation is essential before shaving or waxing as it removes dead skin, which is generally why you get unwanted ingrown hairs. Ensure your legs are well exfoliated, shaved and moisturised, especially when wearing a dress or skirt.

Dry skin brushing helps with circulation, making the legs look radiant and feel super energised. Massage is another way to do this. You can do your own leg massage every day using pure plant and essential oils. The oils I use are juniper berry, cypress, grapefruit and black pepper as they are great for promoting fresh blood to your legs, assisting with breaking up and preventing any cellulite, congestion, fluid retention, varicose and spider veins.

HOT LEGS – MASSAGE OIL BLEND

50ml glass bottle
50ml jojoba oil
5 drops juniper berry pure essential oil
5 drops cypress pure essential oil
5 drops grapefruit pure essential oil
3 drops black pepper pure essential oil

Spend some time each evening massaging this oil into your ankles, calves and thighs, using firm kneading strokes up and down your legs. Stretch for five minutes and then spend at least 10 minutes lying down with your legs up the wall, to improve circulation.

ORGANIC FACE LIFT

"Don't compare your life to that of others; you never know what their journey is all about."

This is a super high-antioxidant mask that works on softening and brightening the skin evening out the skin tone. Alpha hydroxy acids are found in fruit, red wine and dairy and work by dissolving dead skin cells, allowing for a fresher and healthier skin to surface. Green tea and rosehip oil are both especially high in skin protective antioxidants. Use this mask the morning of a big event if you wish to have a radiant, dewy and sparkling complexion.

1 tbsp pink clay
1 organic green tea bag
1 tsp fresh papaya, apple or lemon juice
2 drops rosehip oil

Allow one organic green tea bag to sit in a cup for one hour in just enough purified water to cover it. In a small ceramic dish, gently mix all the mask ingredients together, including a tablespoon of the green tea water concentrate. If the mask is too runny, add a little more pink clay; if it is too thick, add a little more green tea water. Immediately apply the mask to your face, neck and décolletage using small circular motions with your fingertips. Place two chilled green tea bags over each eyelid, lie down and relax while you wait for the mask to activate. Unwind for 15 minutes before rinsing off the mask with cold water. Follow by spraying the skin with an organic facial mist and conclude with a facial massage using your favourite facial oil.

PUPPY PREVENTION

"The purity of a person's heart can be quickly measured by how they regard animals."

PREVENTION SHAMPOO
Animals have skin sensitivities just as humans do. Sodium laureth sulphate, or sodium lauryl sulphate and synthetic fragrances all contribute to irritating skin conditions. Cheap supermarket and veterinary pet shampoos can be harsh on animal skin. Make your own inexpensive pet shampoo by using ingredients that gently clean their fur and skin without causing dryness, and leave behind the fresh scent of pure essential oils. Prevention shampoo is sodium laureth sulphate free and sodium lauryl sulphate free and contains pure essential oils that have been successfully proven to help repel fleas. Wet the animal's coat with warm water and apply a sufficient quantity of shampoo to create a rich lather. Leave on for up to three minutes and rinse thoroughly. Blow-dry and style as normal!

YOU WILL NEED
250ml liquid castile soap
10 drops lavender pure essential oil
4 drops tea tree pure essential oil
8–10 drops essential oil solubiliser
In the bottle of castile soap, carefully combine all the ingredients and shake well. Always label and date home-made products. The shampoo will keep for up to two years.

PREVENTION MIST
If you are concerned about your beloved pooch hitting the town and picking up fleas or nasty germs, make this easy multipurpose spray especially for your furry friend... It can be used pre-walk and as a natural deodorant, sanitizer and flea repellent. Simply mist around the paw and collar areas.

YOU WILL NEED
125ml amber bottle
125ml purified water
6 drops lavender pure essential oil
2 drops tea tree pure essential oil
6–8 drops essential oil solubiliser

Carefully combine all the ingredients in the amber bottle and shake well. Always label and date home-made products. The mist will keep for six months to a year.

For information visit
WWW.PET-HEALTH-ADVISOR.COM

REMEDY SPRAY

"What others think of you is none of your business."

Remedy spray can be used as hydrating facial water or be sprayed onto sore muscles, pimples, burns, mouth ulcers, bites and boils. When magnesium is applied to the skin, it is absorbed very quickly and then it is able to do what it does best: restore cellular levels, maintain proper muscle function and encourage healthy skin tissue. Because lavender pure essential oil is so good for so many things we call it the mother of all pure essential oils. It will do everything in its power to calm redness of the skin, soothe irritation and act as an anti-inflammatory to sore muscles.

100ml glass spray bottle
100ml purified spring water
¼ tsp magnesium chloride powder
5 drops lavender pure essential oil
5 drops essential oil solubiliser

Carefully combine all the ingredients in the glass spray bottle and shake well. Always label and date home-made products. The remedy spray will keep for up to three months, and can be refrigerated for extra cooling and soothing effects during summer.

SKIN FOOD

"I love and respect myself, so I can love and respect others."

The skin reflects the state of our internal health. Treat your outer body just as you would your inner body, by using only 100 per cent natural ingredients to cleanse and nourish your skin. Whatever you use on your skin is absorbed into the bloodstream. Many underestimate this intimate connection and continue to use synthetic and toxic skincare products. These products have no nutritional value and build up in your system causing health problems and toxicity.

Throw away your non-natural skincare products and start formulating skincare that comes from the natural world; use plants, herbs, seeds, clays, nuts, oils and pure essential oils. DIY skincare is the cheapest and most effective way to care for your skin, and once you experience the rejuvenating benefits of natural, organic skincare it is impossible to return to artificially perfumed and synthetic skin product trash. Here are some highly effective and natural skincare ingredients.

- 100 per cent pure essential oils
- 100 per cent pure cold pressed plant oils
- Himalayan rock salt
- Magnesium powder
- Mineral clays
- Non-nano zinc oxide
- Free-range eggs
- Oats
- Fruits and vegetables
- Loose leaf herbal tea
- Cocoa powder
- Shea and cocoa butter
- Ground nuts and seeds
- Linseeds
- Bicarbonate of soda
- Beeswax

- Coconut, almond, oat and goat's milk
- Raw honey
- Distilled floral waters
- Rice bran and rice bran oil
- Seaweed
- Irish moss
- Spirulina
- Vegetable glycerine
- Agar agar
- Xanthium gum
- Sago
- Yoghurt
- Turmeric powder
- Almond meal
- Cinnamon and ginger powder

SKIN FUNGUS

"Never judge another man until you have walked in his shoes."

Fungal infections of the skin are caused by the fungi that reside on your body. A fungus thrives in warm, moist conditions. You need a strong blend of parasitic anti-micro fungal and antifungal pure essential oils to treat skin fungal infections. Combine pure essential oils with a soothing and repairing base oil to care for different skin infections, bacterial infections and fungal infections. Coconut oil is a great base oil to use because it is naturally anti bacterial and antifungal. Symptoms of skin fungus and parasitises include itchiness, redness, and blotchy, flaky and white-spotted patchy marks. The skin fungus ointment can also be used for athlete's foot, warts and toenail disease.

50g glass jar
50g coconut oil
8 drops lavender pure essential oil
4 drops patchouli pure essential oil
4 drops tea tree pure essential oil
2 drops oregano pure essential oil
2 drops bergamot pure essential oil

In a sterilised bowl combine the coconut oil with all the pure essential oils. Thoroughly stir using a clean spoon until you think all the pure essential oils have dispersed into the coconut oil. Spoon into an airtight glass jar and keep away from heat and sunlight. The skin fungus ointment can be topically applied to the affected areas, using clean hands or a cotton tip, two to three times a day until the fungus is gone.

SORE TUMMY OIL BLEND

"The solar plexus chakra relates to one's personal power and is linked to feelings of fear, resentment, self-esteem and trust."

Use this custom-made aromatherapy massage oil whenever you have the uncomfortable symptoms of irritable bowel syndrome, PMS, constipation, flatulence and indigestion. Abdominal massage gently releases tension and toxins in the area. Clary sage is an effective analgesic that helps alleviate pain. Spearmint and fennel oil are good for digestion.

1 tbsp sesame oil
2 drops clary sage pure essential oil
1 drop fennel pure essential oil
1 drop spearmint pure essential oil

Gently massage the stomach rotating in clockwise and anticlockwise movements, for at least five minutes. Lay flat on your back, take deep breaths and think positive and happy thoughts about yourself and all the people in your life. Be sure to consult an aromatherapist to check if the above pure essential oils are suitable for you and consult your practitioner if digestive problems persist.

THE ALCHEMIST

"When you're in-line with your spirit, you will be continually energised by your life's work."

Making your own creams empowers a person to get creative, tailoring their skincare products to be specific for whatever their skin requires at the time. The skin is often changing, depending on diet, environment and age. Creams are a mixture of oil and water blended together with an emulsifier to form a stable mix and this is referred to as an emulsion. All emulsions, from a light cleansing milk, light body lotions through to richer double creams have the same basic ingredients.

REQUIRED EQUIPMENT
2 Hot plates
2 Pyrex glass measuring jugs
2 Thermometers
2 Vegetable steamers or egg rings
2 Saucepans
1 Set of measuring spoons
1 Electric stick blender

BALANCING FACE CREAM – FOR ALL SKIN TYPES

- The oil phase

80ml (4 tbsp) apricot kernel oil
10g grated cocoa butter
10g 100 per cent plant derived emulsifying wax

- The water phase

80ml (4 tbsp) lavender distilled water
1ml (20 drops) citrus seed extract

- Add below 40°C

5 drops lavender pure essential oil
3 drops geranium pure essential oil
1ml (20 drops) evening primrose oil

METHOD FOR MAKING YOUR CREAM

1. Weigh all your ingredients, ensuring measurements are 100 per cent accurate.

2. Place the oil phase ingredients - the apricot kernel oil, cocoa butter and emulsifying wax - into a Pyrex glass measuring jug.

3. Pour your water phase ingredients - the lavender water and citrus seed extract - into another Pyrex glass measuring jug.

4. Place the two glass jugs into two separate saucepans filled with water. The jugs should sit on a vegetable steamer or egg rings inside the saucepan so that they are not sitting directly on the bottom of the saucepan. This ensures the ingredients will not overheat.

5. Place one thermometer into each of the jugs so you can monitor the heating stages of both your oil and water ingredients then place both saucepans onto the stove and begin to heat at a medium to high temperature.

6. Using a spoon, occasionally stir the oil phase ingredients, ensuring the cocoa butter melts properly. Constantly observe the temperature of both the oil and water phases and don't be alarmed if one phase heats more than the other, just remove from the hot plate for a moment and allow the other phase to catch up.

7. When both the water and oil phases have reached 65-70°C, slowly pour the water phase into the oil phase whilst keeping the oil phase jug sitting in the saucepan in the hot water. Stir continuously while doing this. Note that it is okay if the water is at 67°C and the oil is at 70°C as long as they are both around 65-70°C when they are combined.

8. Once all the water phase ingredients have been combined into the oil phase, remove the jug from the heat. The emulsion will be a very watery consistency and will look somewhat milky.

9. Continue stirring to ensure separation does not occur. Use an electric stick blender for 20 to 30 seconds, as using an electric blender whips too much air into the emulsion. If the emulsion is a water-in-oil emulsion that contains more oil than water, stir slowly and steadily so that air bubbles are not incorporated as this may cause the emulsion to separate. Run your spoon regularly over the bottom of the jug to ensure proper homogenisation of all the ingredients.

10. When the emulsion cools to below 45°C (use the thermometer to check this), add the evening primrose, lavender and geranium pure essential oils, and stir in thoroughly using a clean spoon.

11. Once the emulsion becomes thick and perfectly creamy, spoon the mixture into a sterilised airtight glass jar.

12. Now that your cream has cooled, cap and label your jar. Include on your label the purpose and properties of your cream, the ingredients and the date it was made. It is a good idea to take notes when making skincare products because it allows you to perfect the cream each time you make it. Documenting skincare recipes is necessary if you plan to sell your cream commercially.

PROBLEMS WITH MAKING CREAMS

If the recipe is followed strictly, especially the temperatures, you should have a successful batch of creams every time. When you first combine all the ingredients together, the cream is very liquid and runny. This is normal, so don't panic. Once the mixture begins to cool it will thicken; how thick it gets will depend on the amount of water and the types of oils, waxes and fats you use. The more water and the lighter the oils, the lighter the cream will be. The main problem you may encounter in making an emulsion is that it will separate – the oil sits on top and it is watery underneath. This occurs for a number of reasons:

- Inaccurate temperatures when mixing the oil and water phases. Try gently reheating and stirring until combined.

- Hand stirring. Many recipes will suggest hand stirring an emulsion, however I have found it is much better to use a stick blender for a few seconds to prevent separation.

- Emulsifying wax is not incorporated into the oil phase, or the correct amount is not used. You can try melting the emulsifying wax and then incorporating it into the mix and blending. You may find that the mixture remains unstable so leave it standing for a while and mix it later.

THE BALM

"You cannot ever possess anything in the physical world, it's all just borrowed."

It's great to have something that does everything. This balm is one of those all rounder products that treats everything from sunburn, insect bites, skin rashes and irritations to cuts, burns, abrasions and inflammation. Balms and ointments are made from oils, waxes and fats and contain no water. They remain on the surface of the skin for longer than a cream and offer supreme skin protection. This recipe can be used as a massage balm, facial ointment, nappy rash balm, hair treatment and serum, or a lip and temple balm.

15g beeswax
5g cocoa butter
5g shea butter
5g manuka honey
60ml jojoba oil

1. Turn the stove top up to a high heat.

2. Melt the beeswax, cocoa and shea butter in a Pyrex measuring jug and rest it on a vegetable steamer that sits in a saucepan of water.

3. Add the jojoba oil and honey, keeping the mixture over the heat. It may seize up a little when adding any cold ingredients, but they will dissolve once heated.

4. Once the mixture is liquid, remove from the heat.

5. Using an electric stick blender, mix the ingredients to ensure the honey is well dispersed and not sinking to the bottom.

6. Once the mixture begins to cool, stir in any pure essential oils and plant oils you wish.

7. Pour into a glass airtight jar. Add a label stating the purpose and properties of your balm, the ingredients and the date.

When the balm base turns opaque and cools down you can create your own remedial balms for any condition by adding 100 per cent pure essential oils and plant oils that enhance the function of the balm. You will need to thoroughly stir in any pure essential oils and plant oils that you wish to add to the balm base.

To use the balm as a natural deep heat ointment add – 3 drops of lavender, 2 drops of ginger, 3 drops of clove and 3 drops of peppermint pure essential oils.

To use the balm as an anti-ageing night balm, add – 2 drops of frankincense, 2 drops of neroli and 2 drops of rose otto pure essential oils.

To use the balm as a healing nappy rash ointment add – 5 drops of calendula oil, 2 drops of lavender and 1 drop of chamomile pure essential oil.

A SACRED SPACE

"Your mind is the architect of your experience. There is no limit to what it can create"

As an intuitive healer, aromatherapy alchemist and meditation teacher I very strongly believe in treating the body and mind holistically. We need to take care of our physical and energetic bodies with exercise, energy healing, meditation and a healthy diet; and nurture our mind with relaxation, stimulation and creative inspiration. The act of creativity is a sacred process, which can help us to work through stress and stimulate us in ways that enable us to open our heart space and discover inner joy. When we apply ourselves in creative practice we get to the core of our being, discovering parts of ourselves otherwise left untouched. Creativity can imbue every part of our lives, from when we put together an outfit for the day, to when we cook a meal with love, or through the creative choices we make when setting up our home space with cushions, art and ornaments. It doesn't have to be literally sitting down with a paintbrush, but this can be a very cathartic way of being creative, zoning out with some paint and seeing what unfolds. Making our own aromatherapy and skin care preparations is also a very simple, yet satisfying creative act which results in products you are excited about and proud to use.

SWEET VELVET LIP BALM

You will need:
10g beeswax, 10g cocoa butter, 10g shea butter, 25ml olive oil, 1 teaspoon organic vanilla essence, 1 teaspoon organic, raw honey, 4 drops organic orange essential oil (could also use peppermint oil), Pyrex jug, saucepan, egg ring, kitchen scales, 4 sterile 15g lip balm jars with lids

Method
Measure and weigh your ingredients. Turn the hot plate on medium, heating about 3 inches of water in the bottom of a medium sized saucepan. Once bubbling add the egg ring, and place the Pyrex jug on top of the egg ring (which keeps the bottom of the jug from touching the bottom of the saucepan). Add the beeswax, shea butter, and cocoa butter into the jug, stirring with a spoon. Allow to melt, and then add the olive oil, honey and vanilla essence. Once all ingredients are mixed through and completely liquid take off the heat. Once it begins to cool (after about 2 min) add your essential oils. While still liquid carefully pour your mixture into the lip balm jars slowly filling to just below the top. Allow to set before putting the lid on. This will make 4 lip balms, keep one or two for yourself and give to family or friends as a gift with a cute sticker and a description of your creation. To make a softer balm add 5 ml more oil, to make firmer add 5g more cocoa butter, or experiment to find a texture you like. For a vegan version omit the beeswax and honey and replace with an extra 5ml of olive oil and an extra 10g shea butter and 5g cocoa butter.

Visit WWW.ALYSSUMALCHEMY.COM.AU and subscribe to the Alyssum Alchemy blog for more inspiring ways to Live a Sacred Life.

CHAPTER SEVEN

SELF-HELP – AKA HIPPY ADVICE

"Life is for learning. It is a voyage of self-discovery and growth. Obtaining happiness and peace in life requires both action and introspection. To find our true life purpose we must reflect, listen, participate and be willing to change. Self-help is a productive path to personal and spiritual development. Enjoy your special journey of self-realisation..."

ALWAYS TAKE THE WEATHER WITH YOU

"All of humanity's problems stem from man's inability to quieten the mind."

Many of us make the mistake of believing that if we are somewhere else or with someone else we would be happier – on holidays, with a new partner, in a different house or five kilos skinnier.

The truth is we wouldn't! Whatever circumstances and life lessons you are working through are happening for a reason – so you can learn, grow and evolve. If your mental state is negative and you continually wish things were different, it doesn't matter where you go, or who you are with – your troubles will always follow you.

Life is for learning... We have to accept the challenges that come our way, breathe through tough times and learn from the lessons that come from them. We may find that our journey is beautiful, confronting and complicated all at once, but that's okay. Life is for learning...

AN AFFAIR TO REMEMBER

"Any chef can make you enjoy the first bite of a meal, but only a chef that cooks with love can make you enjoy the last."

There is no greater love than the love of food. It is a passion and ongoing relationship. The way it looks, the way it smells, the way it brings people together. A passionate cook will adore the relaxed state of mind cooking brings, followed by the intense, almost selfish satisfaction received when others immensely enjoy the food prepared.

When your whole life revolves around food, you begin to ask yourself what it actually is that motivates this indescribable love. Food represents health, culture, unity and contentment. Cooking allows one to express love, through the nurturing practice of feeding others.

They say cooking is an art, a meditation and a craft. Cookery is a spiritual practice, an opportunity for the busy mind to be still, stepping outside the conscious. When one is in this state, it is where the soul is authorised to truly express itself. Food preparation must not only be hygienically clean and nutritionally sound, but the cook must prepare it with sincerity and in a well intentioned way.

Cooking is either a natural gift or self-taught and practised, and is one of the most empowering gifts a person can have. The success of cooking great meals can only come from a place of deep appreciation and respect that a fine cook has for food. Research an organised cooking class in your area; download the cooking and food iPhone applications. Begin your first cook off by exploring the recipes of your favourite cultures and their cuisine and give the recipes a go in your own kitchen. People should not fear cooking, as with anything in life, you must believe in yourself and you'll generate something magical.

Learn how to cook holistically at:
WWW.VEGIEHEAD.COM
WWW.NOURISHEDKITCHEN.COM

ANSWER YOUR CALLING

"If there is no struggle, there will be no progress. Embrace the challenge, growth awaits..."

Pick up the damn telephone; it's your soul calling to tell you to stop doing whatever you're doing in your life that is making you unhappy. Are you are in a job that doesn't make your heart sing? Are you in a relationship that doesn't feel whole? Do you continue to hang around with people that deep down you know you have outgrown? Listen to your inner self. It tells you the steps you need to take to discard those things you no longer need to evolve and progress in life.

Okay, I understand it may not be practical to walk into work tomorrow and quit; immediately file for divorce; or stroll into uni and defer your degree. All I am saying is why bang your head against a wall year after year pretending to be happy when you really feel lost? Life is not meant to be hard. As humans on this planet we have choice. We can be whatever we want to be, follow the flow of our own path, and listen to that calling of our own heart. Unfortunately many of us take the call waiting option, and procrastinate when it comes to taking a leap of courage, because we are fearful we will not make the right decision.

Nothing is impossible and whatever you truly spiritually desire will always happen for you. Start to manifest all the things you, not your ego, really want. Visualise yourself having a career that excites you, kissing a lover that you see as your soulmate and being in the company of friends that inspire you. After all, if you want something bad enough the universe can't help but give it to you!

AWARENESS

"Health and wellness only take place when your body gets the nutrients it needs to flourish."

I'm not a huge fan of following any diet too closely. I believe that life and nutrition is not so cut and dry, and a good eating plan should be one that you can sustain forever. There are way too many conflicting approaches to diet that all take a different angle, from lifestyle, blood type and body type to religion, tradition and genetics.

The only diet plans I will ever bow down to are those that are the oldest and most influential, including the Ayurvedic, Tibetan and Traditional Chinese Medicine approaches to diet. My advice is to take a little of everything and listen carefully to your body and what it responds to. You can always count on presenting symptoms to tell you what is right for you. The physical signs your body likes the food you are eating are more energy, better sleep, a lighter feeling, clear skin, bright eyes and no physical pain. Emotional signs are happiness, clarity, relaxation, mental alertness and contentment.

Some people feel incredibly inspired about strictly following a diet that makes them feel good. That's cool and if you truly feel complete then your entire body must want to eat that way. The only way of eating I am consistently strict with is eating a 100 per cent unprocessed and natural diet of fresh wholefoods. I kind of roll in and out of different health plans, depending on what I feel like – some weeks I don't eat meat, some weeks I do. For a few months I only eat organic and wildcrafted foods, sometimes I try to save cash and don't. Other times I'm Asian influenced and cook fresh fish and rice for breakfast; at times my diet follows the Mediterranean way so much that I have olive oil seeping out of my pores.

I will quickly wrap things up by saying, enjoy exploring the path to good health, don't be afraid to mix it up and try new things. Always keep in mind your trusty intuition and precious body knows best; just listen and feel.

EAT WHEN YOU'RE HUNGRY

"We live in a world where half the population is overweight and the other half are starving."

Honour your body and eat when you need food. It is best to eat when you are hungry because then the body is eager to absorb nutrients and convert the food to energy. It is important to listen to the body rather than the mind when it comes to meal times and food choices. Do not deprive yourself if you are genuinely hungry, and learn to tell the difference between mind hunger and body hunger. When the mind is hungry it is often because we are stressed, bored, restless, out of balance and not content. When the body is hungry you feel empty and your physical being craves wholesome foods that restore and nourish you.

Most of us distract ourselves during meal times by watching television or working at the computer. Try to make a conscious effort to eat in a peaceful place where you can appreciate your meals, enjoying their smells, textures and tastes. It is important to stop eating when your body is satisfied, because eating until you are painfully full places unnecessary strain on the digestive system.

Tips for mindful eating:
WWW.TINYBUDDHA.COM

GET LOST

"Until you make peace with who you are, you will never be happy with what you have."

Feeling lost is a necessary stage of personal growth. When we feel lost, it brings us to a place where we can find ourselves, discover who we are, what we want, and most importantly, how we as individuals can make a difference in this world of ours.

Travel is one of the best ways to discover your true and authentic self. When we are out of our comfort zone and become vulnerable, we have no choice but to be ourselves. Open, present and spontaneous is the best travel headspace. Completely surrender to the experience, be open to whatever comes your way, and let the experience unfold organically. Be grateful for whatever flows and take this new mentality back to your reality, wherever that may be in life.

For more information on wellbeing travel escapes visit:
WWW.TOUCHOFSPIRITTOURS.COM.AU

GOAL SETTING

"We are here on Earth to transform ourselves into something worth being proud of."

The way to realistically decide what we want in the future and how we will get it, is firstly to know where we are right now, and secondly, to determine how satisfied we are in our current situation. Strategic goal setting is highly effective as it helps us become clear about where we want to be, how to achieve what we desire, and then evaluate and reflect on progress so the growth can be measured.

DREAMS

What are your dreams and goals? These are not related to the past or what you thought you wanted, but to what you want now. Have you ever sat down and really thought through your life and determined what you really want? These are the true dreams and goals that come from your heart, spirit and mind; the goals that are unique to you and come from who you were created to be and are able to become.

VALUES

When you know who you are, you have a clearer understanding of where you are going. Make a list of all the things you feel strongly about. For example, kindness, honesty, money, marriage, family, career, love, fun or perhaps, education. Everybody's values and belief systems are different depending on their past experiences. It is important to be clear what your true values and beliefs are.

SPECIFY

Get specific and make a list of all the things you want for your future. Start with a short list of all the things you wish to achieve in the next six months, then write a list of things you aspire to achieve in the next two years. Accountability – who, how and what is going to help you achieve your goals? Make a step by step list of how you plan to achieve your goals. Every goal should have a time frame attached to it; life is much more productive this way.

Setting goals is an incredibly exciting process, because it allows you to establish what you want in life and a strategy to achieve it. Remember that your thoughts create your experiences. If you want something with all your heart, all you have to do is focus on it, and you will be granted the power to accomplish your dreams. Life is spooky like that; try it.

LIFE IS SWEET

"A trouble shared is a trouble halved."

As you grow older you become more and more okay with who you are and happy to just be. You only wish to spend time with those people who are kind, like-minded, genuine, honest and wholesome. You begin to understand the flow of life a little more, respect your body and develop the wisdom to trust yourself. You become aware that it's important to value your physical body. You become hit with some kind of cosmic realisation that life is really about learning and spiritual development.

A chapter of life is now over, a chapter that tells a story of self-doubt, worry and fear is now laid to rest. You are reminded that it is your divine birthright to be happy, and that suffering is an individual choice that you can give up at any time. We discover that emotions like greed, envy, fear and jealousy are useless, and no longer serve us. Happiness becomes a comfortable place where everything is in divine and perfect order, and for our highest good.

Life is sweet.

MIND FULLNESS

"Your body deserves respect. Be mindful about the food you eat, how you eat it and where you buy it. This encourages wise food choices and healthy eating habits."

Mindful of origin – Source local and sustainable food at farmers markets, fruit shops and health food stores. The journey that each ingredient in your food has gone through is important because it affects the quality and vibration of your food dramatically. Eating jet-lagged food is not ideal for your health. Local, organic, wildcrafted, biodynamic is much more conducive to energy and vitality.

Mindful of portion – This is one of the biggest lessons I have learned about food, partly due to the fact that my cooking tastes so damn good and partly due to the fact that I tend to eat for contentment. We don't need big meals. In actual fact we get more nutrients from our meals if they are smaller and chewed more slowly, as the body can then deal with digesting one thing at a time carefully and effectively.

Mindful of food preparation – Be mindful about your dietary requirements and how you can retain and enhance as many nutrients as possible. It is best not to overcook food, let it go rancid or eat food that is not ripe or in season. Cook with care, love and intention and you will feel energised, nurtured and satisfied.

Mindful of destination – Food that sits in a glass window under bright lights in some greasy 24 hour takeaway shop or petrol station is dead food. It's not nutritious, or wholesome, and probably possesses ingredients that are very bad for you. Choose family run, modest, organic, traditional cafés and restaurants that sell fresh cooked meals.

Mindful of company – Try to eat your meals with people you love and care about as often as you can. This suggestion may sound strange, however, people need to understand that energetically our emotions affect our digestive system and it's important to be relaxed and happy when you eat.

Mindful of impact – Buy food that is in season. Out of season fruits and vegetables have usually travelled vast distances to get to you. Don't waste food. It is easy to forget that producing food uses water and energy so the waste goes way back down the line. Every thing is good in season.

MONKEY MIND

"We are trying to beat the system, find our rhythm in the madness."

Think about what you want, rather than what you don't want. Our thoughts create our experiences and it is incredibly important to practise control over your thoughts. It is equivalent of putting your hands on the steering wheel of your life. Although thoughts that contribute to worry, guilt, fear, judgment and jealousy are considered somewhat normal, remember do not serve you. These thoughts lead to unhappiness. A calm mind is a happy mind, and we really do have control over how we think. Don't give your mind permission to house negative thoughts, or indulge in negativity; if you find your mind gets the better of you try these thoughts:

Self-talk for perspective – Remind yourself to stop thinking negative thoughts, because they are thoughts that don't serve you. Remember you are blessed to be given the gift of life, and you are always guided and being taken care of. Tell yourself, "I have a roof over my head, I have friends and family, enough money for food, and I have been given the gift of life..." Everybody has something to be grateful for.

Yoga and Meditation – Yoga and meditation promote self-awareness and self-discipline as well as mental clarity and emotional stability. The mind is just like any muscle in the body, it requires training for strength and optimum results. Positive practices like yoga and meditation strengthen nerve activity in the brain which helps regulate behaviour.

The present moment – Constantly bring yourself to the present moment. Yes, right here, right now. Take a look around and notice the small things, the details, the smells and the sounds that surround you right now. The past is dust, the future is untold, and all we have is now, so enjoy and relax – everything will flow organically as it is supposed to if you are in the present moment.

Aromatherapy – Burn rosemary, basil, frankincense, lemon and lime pure essential oils. These aromas are wonderful for mental clarity and encourage the mind to stay calm and clear. Have a bath, get a massage, do something to nurture yourself, as quite often all we need is a little self-love to feel better.

Do something – You may notice that we are guilty of distracting ourselves. Often we turn to self-destructive methods like smoking, drinking alcohol, drugs, food, material possessions and emotional dependencies. Try throwing yourself into something creative like writing, painting or photography. Just do it, you may uncover a hidden creative talent. You may discover something outside your mind takes over and before you know it, your soul starts to sing. Fill your time with things you like to do.

MORNING IDENTITY

To know yourself, you must forget yourself."

The morning is such a valuable time for serenity and solitude; spend some time alone and enjoy the present. Use this time to cultivate inner peace and set your intention for the day. Dedicate 10 minutes in the morning to the following chakra balance meditation.

Begin by sitting or kneeling in a comfortable position on the floor; you can use a pillow or cushion for extra comfort and support. The breath is our life force – breathe. Sit straight and tall, close your eyes and take some deep breaths in through your nose and out through your mouth. Feel your lower body on the ground, relax your shoulders, be aware of the sounds inside and outside, and continue to breathe.

Base – Gently hold onto your ankles and visualise the colour red. Say to yourself: I am supported by the planet. "I am supported by life. I am grateful for the lessons I have learnt and the foundation of who I am. I remember all the things I hoped for when I was a child. I am balanced and supported."

Sacral – Gently rest yours hands on your lower abdomen and visualise the colour orange. Say to yourself: "I am a joyful being. I release all sadness and concerns about my sexuality. I am free to have fun, and happiness is my divine birthright. I am creative, sexually open and seek pleasure and joy in every moment. Life is sweet."

Solar – Gently rest your hands on the middle of your stomach and visualise the colour yellow. Say to yourself: "I let go of anger towards myself and others; I completely accept myself and others from this day onwards; I release being a worrier; I let go of the past and trust that the future is bright. I live in harmony with myself and others."

Heart – Gently rest your hands on the centre of your chest and visualise the colour green. Say to yourself: "I love freely and openly; I show compassion to all the people I meet and unlock my heart to others; I am open to give and receive love. Love is everything and is everywhere."

Throat – Gently rest your hands on the front of your neck and visualise the colour blue. Say to yourself: "I only speak the truth; my opinions are valid; communication is valuable and productive; and I listen attentively to others. I honour the fact that my words are powerful and I respect the great importance of listening and speaking."

Third eye – Gently rest your two index fingers in the middle of your eyebrows and visualise the colour indigo. Say to yourself: "My intuition is my greatest gift; I trust my inner knowledge, and there is no need for me to over-analyse situations. I allow information to flow freely in and out."

Crown – Raise your hands to the top of your head and gently rest them upon the crown. Visualise white or gold light radiating above your head and say to yourself: "I no longer need to search for answers outside myself; I trust my higher self; I need not fear the unknown. I seek enlightenment and invite spirituality into my life."

Conclude this morning mediation by taking a few deep breaths in through the nose and out through the mouth. Write any thoughts that come to you in a journal and explore how it feels to say the mantras. Enjoy a day of balance and inner peace.

Namaste.

MUMBO

The purpose of having children is to create more good people for the world."

One of the biggest challenges a mother faces is finding time for herself. The daily pressure and exhaustion of attending to children's needs often results in stress and depression. Being a mother is one of the most rewarding and honourable roles you can have as a woman, but it is very important to allocate time to recharging and nourishing yourself. Over the years I have held workshops for mothers on stress management, and the feedback I get is that these women feel they don't have time, or feel guilty about making the time, to simply do something for themselves. I wish to share with you some helpful stress management techniques for yourself and your children.

Yoga – If you can't get to a class, make time to practise at home – buy a yoga book or movie and stretch for 20 minutes. Yoga makes life easier, because it gives you the energy and peace you need to deal with life's challenges.

Massage – Schedule a professional monthly massage. If this is not financially possible, do your own self-massage using pure essential oils and plant oils. Massage relieves tension and balances the entire nervous system.

Bathing – Make time for a bath, either late at night, or before sunrise. Bathing is the classic way to dissolve stress and tension, it can also relieve the physical strain a mother holds in her body from lifting and bending. A bath containing pure essential oils of geranium, lavender and rose is perfect.

Nutrition – Simple, wholesome home-cooked food is best for yourself and your family. What is more important, time or health? Diet affects everything including our physical and emotional behaviour.

Aromatherapy – Burn and vaporise pure essential oils that relax both mother and baby. Lavender, mandarin, chamomile, and sandalwood oils are ideal.

Nature time – Nothing beats a family event like a bush walk, a day at the beach or a picnic in the park. These are healthy, inexpensive and perfect ways to connect with your family.

Ocean swimming – Take your children swimming at the beach as often as possible. The ocean is one of the best ways to cleanse, refresh and energise your being.

Music – A house of music is a house of fun and inspiration. Play music: jazz, old school classics, world music. Pick up a second-hand keyboard, ukulele, or mini guitar and encourage your children to get musical.

Child-minding swap – Create a structured roster with someone in your family or circle of friends, about child-minding swap: you can look after the children Friday morning for one hour while they go to yoga, and they can look after them on Saturday afternoon while you get a massage.

PERFECT PASSION

"Passion is the most important ingredient in the recipe of life."

When you share your passion with others, there is an unseen energy that radiates all around you. It is acknowledged and felt by everyone. Passion attracts success and fulfilment and the effects can be astounding. When you speak with true passion it comes through in your tone of voice, your mannerisms and the complete joy you embody. People connect with passion because it's authentic, it real. Honouring your passions directly unites you with your true purpose for living. To be successful you must have 90 per cent passion and 10 per cent talent. Passion is the key ingredient to becoming excited about your life.

To become aware of your passions try the following exercise –
In a quiet place, grab a pen and paper. Sit upright with your feet on the ground in order to connect with your true self. Make a list of your Top 10 passions. These should not be things you used to love, or what others think you enjoy. These are your present spiritual, emotional and physical passions that truly bring you the greatest joy and pleasure and make your heart sing.

PHILOSOPHICAL HIPPY ADVICE

"Living a holistic lifestyle makes you feel like a whole person."

Each day we are given an opportunity to live and learn. A truly peaceful mind comes from letting ourselves know that everything, I mean everything, will be alright in our lives. The purpose of life should always be about self-healing, self-balance and self-discovery. Life is a journey that involves work, effort and compromise.

See the beauty in everyday things like the sky, the moon, the flowers, the local coffee man – everything. Always forgive; we are all doing our best in learning our life's lessons. Believe in your divine right to happiness. Forget about trivial problems, in the big picture it doesn't really matter. Perspective – living in a cardboard box is a real problem, someone gossiping about you is not a problem.

Express your creativity as this allows your true character to shine. Know you are protected and guided on this journey; nothing is a coincidence. Believe in the power of destiny. The universe has a plan for us... work with it, not against it. You construct your own luck, success and prosperity. Results come from opening your mind, listening and taking action with the knowledge you acquire. Our spirit needs cleansing. Trust your intuition and heart. We need to love ourselves, so that we can love others even more. We are all sexual creatures, embrace this, and express your sexuality in an uplifting way.

You deserve. Everything is yours if you want it; just ask for it. First, be clear about your intention. Let go of fear; fear limits your life. Through your beliefs and faith you can purify your mind of negativity. Think about what you spiritually desire. Your journey is your own.

For more information on living a mindful life visit WWW.ELEPHANTJOURNAL.COM

PREVENTION

"In health there is freedom. Health is the first of all liberties... Every human being is the creator of his health or disease."

I don't like spending money at the doctors and pharmacy to cure or treat health problems. Instead I spend my money on healthy organic food and herbal remedies. This seems to create a financial balance because I have to eat regardless, and by eating the best quality food my immunity and health are always at their best, making an expensive trip to the doctors rare.

In the East, the biggest health practice is the prevention method. Spend your time and money on things that prevent illness and disease instead of on pharmaceuticals after they occur. In the West, most people go about their busy lives eating whatever they want without any consideration. They take numerous medications to stabilise medical conditions that go on year after year, without ever actually stopping to consider the underlying cause of the problem.

Becoming healthy and sustaining health requires a positive outlook and consistent maintenance of the body and mind. This is only achieved through a natural diet, regular exercise and spiritual practice. Doing additional things like massage, sauna, bathing and artistic expression will all help to prevent illness and promote a relaxed and healthy lifestyle.

REALISE THE HIDDEN MAGIC OF TODAY

"I love being alive. The food on my plate is healthy. My work is gratifying. I feel blessed that I have a place to lay my head at night - Mantra."

Each day in a notebook or diary write down five things you are grateful for. Get into the daily habit of acknowledging what you already have, rather than what you don't have. By doing this you bring your mind back to the present moment and reflect on all the things that you appreciate in life. This will make more you aware of the simple things you may have taken for granted.

Unhappiness is a result of ego, want and dissatisfaction. We must train ourselves to have gratitude and be thankful for the things we have right now, right here in this moment. It is an illusion to think that happiness only comes from gaining something we don't have; happiness is a result of appreciation and acceptance.

SWEET DREAMS ARE MADE OF THESE...

"Pay attention to your dreams; you are receiving important messages."

Your dreams are a magical story of the events that happen in your life. We are all able to observe and analyse our dreams. The best ways to do this is to record your dream as soon as you wake. A dream journal is good to have, especially for children, as journals are a great read years down the track.

1. Write down whatever you recall about your dream immediately upon awakening; just write any little thing you can remember, the rest of the dream will unravel as you do.

2. Give your dream a theme title, for example "Love."

3. Break down the dream into chapters or a story line of events.

4. What feelings did you have in the dream – worry, fear, bliss or pain?

Now think about what aspect of your life the dream is about – work, money, or family? Recurring dreams signify messages that your higher self and angels are trying to tell you.

Visit WWW.DREAMGUIDE.COM.AU for your online dream interpretation.

TAKE IT EASY

"Follow your heart, never surrender your dreams. Continually work towards your goals. Believe in yourself, and be true to who you are. Take time to enjoy life's pleasures."

Life is like yoga. Each circumstance in which we find ourselves is like a pose. Some poses are hard to hold, others are pleasant. It is how we hold the pose that determines whether or not we will suffer or grow, and whether or not we will listen to the drama of the ego or the wisdom of our spirit. We all have a choice, these choices are neither right nor wrong; they just are. On the yoga mat we learn about patience, acceptance, and flexibility. Through yoga we take these teachings and we naturally have a similar approach to everyday life situations.

Just like life, sometimes the yoga class is fun and invigorating, other times it's challenging and demanding. Throughout life we are required to face a never ending set of circumstances, from which we learn life's lessons. What's important is not to be hard on yourself. Approach life with an open heart and have some fun along the way. Take it easy, lighten up if you can, don't even try to understand. It is wise to say that people should strive not to think so much, but rather feel a little more. Slowly, slowly should be your philosophy in life. Your dreams will come true and your work will get done but if you don't slow down and pace yourself, you will never fully appreciate the process and natural flow.

THE 21ST CENTURY BOHEMIAN

"Be a hippy in your city."

Today the term bohemian is generally used to describe alternative people who live unconventional and artistic lives. The 21st century bohemian describes an individual who lives differently to people who follow a mainstream lifestyle. Currently in the West a mainstream lifestyle refers to people who do not live naturally. They eat processed, artificial food, clean with toxic chemicals, wear mass produced clothing labels, contribute negatively to our environment, depend on pharmaceutical drugs, and purchase synthetic make-up, hair products and artificial supplies. The 21st century bohemian practises a way of life that is opposite to a mainstream life. It is clear that we are all different, and through experience, values and perception our choices are made; it is a great mystery as to what brings us to that place.

One thing that is for sure is that there is an immense shift in attitudes occurring throughout the world. There is a change in human consciousness that revolves around more and more people wanting to turn to a more natural and holistic way of life. There is a higher demand for natural therapists, as more people seek out alternative approaches to medicine and lifestyle. Many theories are talked about and on a subconscious level the human race instinctively knows the world needs change. Perhaps due to detrimental environmental issues, we are feeling there will come a time when we will have to live sustainably and self-sufficiently once again. I know I didn't have a choice to even write this book, it almost wrote me. I just knew I felt obligated to do my bit in contributing to the shift in the world – Namaste.

THE BODY'S INTELLIGENCE

"Such is life."

Your body is highly intelligent. It knows what it wants to eat, it knows when it wants to sleep and it knows when it feels up to exercise. It is not hard to hear the voice of your own body. You will become much healthier and happier if you tune in and listen to it. In Western civilisation people tend to push themselves at work and at their social activities. They ignore fatigue and run on empty, falling into a vicious cycle of topping up the system with coffee, sugar and other stimulants just to get through another hectic day. There is a great danger involved in living this lifestyle because your system is in jeopardy of burn out, and you are potentially inflicting a harmful array of physical and emotional health problems upon yourself.

Pretend you are moving out of your body for a while, and another person is moving in. This is an exercise that will help remind you of what your body needs. Leave a note to the new tenant with a list you think your body requires most, such as I need rest, regular watering, food every three hours, physical contact, daily exercise and sunshine. Looking after your emotional intelligence is equally important because your body hears everything you think and say about it, so be mindful to think positive and loving thoughts about your body. The body and mind are one and for wholeness we must live in loving communion with our bodies.

GOOD LIFE

"La dolce vita - the art of doing nothing is a sweet life."

Feed yourself natural, fresh, real food

Eat a balanced diet of fresh and nutritionally sound food. Organic, biodynamic and wildcrafted food is best. Pure food and water allow you to do everything to your greatest potential in your life. This advice also includes what you feed your skin – only use natural, raw or organic products to cleanse and moisturise the skin.

Visit an alternative health care practitioner at least once

Alternative medicine is one of the most comprehensive medical systems in the world today. This medicine looks at the entire individual on a functional systemic basis that integrates all components of our mental and emotional bodies. A natural therapist treats the cause rather than just the symptoms. A common theme in this practice is the commitment to holistic medicine, treating the whole person physically, mentally, emotionally and spiritually. A good naturopath will take into account the social context in which a person lives, works and relates, and works together with each individual to promote healing in whatever way, and in whichever area it is needed.

Exercise, do yoga and stretch

Yoga of any kind has been shown to ease depression, increase flexibility, keep muscles toned and help us to gain better balance of body and mind. We all know exercise increases endorphins; these are the happy chemicals in our brain that allow us to think clearer, function optimally and feel better about ourselves.

Burn aromatherapy oils in your home and workspace

Trust me with this one. Being surrounded by aromatherapy oils has greatly enhanced my life. Pure essential oils lift the energetic vibration of any environment. This creates feelings of comfort, wellbeing and deep relaxation.

Get good sleep

Everybody is different with the amount of sleep they need. The most important thing about sleeping is not necessarily the quantity, but the quality. A sound night's sleep allows our entire body to regenerate, replenish and rebound back into daily life full of life and energy.

Learn and laugh

Keeping the brain stimulated is one of the best ways we can fight off the signs of ageing. Stay curious, creative and ask questions about the world. It is essential to maintain a playful spirit in order to stay happy. Find laughter throughout the day. See things on the lighter side of life. I promise it will bring great joy.

Get amongst the Nature

Get your feet in the sand as often as you can, have a dip in the ocean and go for a walk in the bush. Spending time alone in nature is important. Being in nature brings us back to our roots, the foundation of who we are. Being amongst animals and plant life allows you to connect with the world, allowing you to connect to your higher self.

Love and be social

Love and appreciate the people you have in your life. Be caring, interested and supportive of your friends, family and partner; learn to love unconditionally and without expectation. Party as often as possible! Try to go along to every lunch, dinner or birthday you get invited to. Being sociable is good for qi and vitality.

Stay spiritual

Giving thanks to the universe, personal god and guru is powerful. Religion is a bridge to spirituality. You don't have to go to a church in order to be spiritual. God is everywhere. Do whatever helps you feel connected to spirit.

Honour who you are

Why be a second rate version of someone else, when you can be a first rate version of yourself? You deserve all that you desire and should honour all that you are. Be a complete and satisfied soul, after all there is only one of you. You are without a doubt, an amazing person. Take time to honour that.

THE TEN HIPPY COMMANDMENTS

"I don't care about what others expect from me. I am here to participate in the work of my higher self. I am not concerned with the expectations and opinions of others."

1. **Read** – Get to know the greats: William Shakespeare, Oscar Wilde, and Charles Dickens. Books are your friends that will teach you more about yourself than you could imagine. Reading educates and inspires your intellectual and creative self.

2. **Travel** – We often forget there is a whole world out there waiting for us to see. If you have the opportunity to travel then do so. Seeing and feeling the vibe of a new place and its culture is one of the most stimulating things you can do. Travel enhances your perspective and adds to your character forever.

3. **Treat all with kindness** – If we were all compassionate the world would be a sensational place. We must be patient, respectful and understanding of one another. Remember that each and every one of us is doing our very best. Learn to accept and co-exist; everyone is on a different journey. Show compassion to those suffering or in a less fortunate place than you.

4. **Forgive** – Let it go, life is too precious to waste a moment on anger and resentment. People will only hurt us if we allow them to. You can spend hours, days, weeks or even months over analysing a situation, trying to put together the pieces, justifying what could've, would've happened... or you can just leave the pieces on the floor and move on.

5. **Fake it to make it** – Even if you don't know what you're doing pretend that you do, until you figure it out. If you don't believe in yourself, no one else will. Just go for it, act as if you know what you're doing and talking about; flow with it and you just might surprise yourself. We are often more capable than we think.

6. **Don't gossip** – Exit conversations that involve talking about another people's business. Indulging in gossip may be interesting and might make you feel in the loop, but it will soon make you feel guilty and will leave you wondering what others are saying about you when you're not around. Take the high road – you'll feel better inside and appear far more content.

7. **Don't be lukewarm** – Be hot, be cold but never be lukewarm about anything or anyone. Life is exciting, get passionate about it. Be happy and excited, and allow the world to see it. Your joy will be infectious, your confidence contagious.

8. **Don't always believe your head** – The body and emotions never lie. The mind, on the other hand, can tell you all sorts of stories if you let it. You are not your mind, don't be ruled by it. Use it when needed, but don't believe all the stories.

9. **Be disciplined** – Life is about balance. Work hard, play hard. Push yourself. Understand that it is satisfying to achieve and get things done but also acknowledge the importance of relaxing and down time. Hard work is how you look it at; it can be as painful or pleasurable as you allow it to be.

10. **Live well** – Eat well, love well, sleep well, exercise well and relax well.

THE TRIPLE PISCES

"Ideal worlds can be created, as we are only as happy as we allow ourselves to be."

As we mature, we gain more life experience. We have been through hurdles, hardship and adversity. We have felt love, felt pain and had people in our life come and go. As we grow older we tend to realise that the small things aren't the end of the world, we see the big picture and develop the life tools to deal with sticky situations. Emotional maturity finds us a little more appreciative, wiser and content.

Life is about throwing yourself out there, getting involved and doing your best in creating unity between the body and mind. As we develop we need to spend time with people that help us expand and most importantly support our emotional and spiritual growth; we should aim to build relationships with people we can learn from. In all relationships it is important to remember to accept each other's differences and respect one another as complete individuals in this world.

It is suggested that we all construct the good and bad circumstances we are faced with; we create the chaos and the peace in our life, and the outcome of our day-to-day existence simply depends on what kind of life we want to lead. We have a choice to create commotion, or generate a peaceful existence... A triple Pisces may just understand this...

TIME OUT

"When you dream of an owl, ask yourself what wisdom you are denying or seeking."

Taking time out to rest and rejuvenate is extremely important. When you cannot give back to yourself, you will never be able to completely give to others. Stress is responsible for 99 per cent of the body's illnesses. In holistic medicine we believe that in order to maintain optimum health and balance, we need to consider our physical, emotional and spiritual wellbeing.

Often people think they do not have one moment for themselves. These people genuinely believe they do not have time, or they are under the impression that they don't deserve to take time out for themselves. This is a self-defeating mentality, and no excuse! When you are under stress, you become deluded into thinking you have no time. There is time, but you are simply too stressed to realise it.

Take the time... put everything and everyone on hold. Get a massage, go to yoga, walk on the beach, play a sport, spend the afternoon in bed reading or go on a holiday. Put yourself first for once and just do it, even if it's only once a month. No job, child, partner, house, family or education is more important than your own health. When you surrender and take the time to give you back to yourself, you will be much more productive and happier for it.

URBAN HIPPY

"It is what it is."

For life to be successful it is essential that we develop certain cardinal virtues. A virtuous person is ever happy, peaceful and prosperous. Throughout history many great spiritual leaders have spoken about leading by example, cultivating peace and being the change you wish to see in others and the world. An urban hippy is an individual who incorporates both urban and hippy lifestyles; he or she may participate in conventional activities, whilst holding core values that support the environment, human happiness and spiritual progression. Every week pick an urban hippy virtue to practise in your life.

Serenity
Be peaceful within yourself. Let that inner peace and joy radiate through a serene frame of mind. A serene person is a peaceful, smiling and grounded individual who does not possess any violent emotions, cause trouble or speak loud and abruptly.

Absence of vanity
Do not boast of your birth, position, financial situation, qualifications and spiritual attainments. Praise others. See good in all. Treat even the lowliest creatures as your equal and with respect. Be humble about your inner and outer fortunes, life is not a caste system and no one is better than anyone else in this world.

Sincerity
Ensure your words match your actions; it is important to live a life that you preach. Let your words agree with your thoughts, let your actions agree with your words, and let there be harmony among your thoughts, words and actions.

Simplicity
Be simple in your existence. Be simple in your dress. Be simple in your food. We often become misled into thinking that material belongings and money bring us happiness. Then we discover that simple things like a beautiful sunset, a hug from a friend and a walk along the beach are the priceless activities that really fill our hearts with joy.

Non-irritability
Irritability is the precursor of violent outbursts of anger. Watch carefully for the disturbance in mental stability. Be patient with yourself and others because no one is perfect. Have compassion for others, and remind yourself you will only get irritated if you allow yourself to feel that way.

Adaptability
Understand the diverse nature of the people with whom you come into contact. Adjust your mode of approach to suit them. Adjust yourself in such a way as to be pleasing to them. Joyfully accept the eccentricities of others. Always react in a harmonious manner. Serve, accept and love all. Remember that a higher power dwells in all our hearts.

Integrity
Learn to become a person of high moral principles. Lead a life of righteousness. Let righteousness, dignity and integrity be the basis of who you are. Be good to others. Live this way of life and you will see that everyone will trust, admire, obey, and respect you.

Nobility
A noble person displays consistent integrity, self-respect and an above average commitment to doing what is right regardless of circumstance. Take a broad view of things. Ignore the faults of others. Be great and noble-minded in whatever you do. Avoid meaningless talk and childish behaviour. Don't allow the mind to dwell on little and insignificant things.

Generosity
Give, give and give. This is the secret of abundance. In whatever you give be liberal. Often when our own needs are not met, we fear giving back to others. Take delight in the joy of others by making them happy. Generosity is a primary virtue that always benefits the giver and receiver.

Purity
Be pure in your heart. Eradicate evil, anger and greed. Be pure in your thoughts and pray for the wellbeing of all. Be pure in your words; never utter harsh, or unkind words. Be pure in body by keeping it clean and healthy.

_O

"The traveler that ventures into the world alone is faced with an immense and powerful opportunity".

Time alone is as essential as breathing. Time to check in with ourselves, to sit in the core of who we are and uncover what's really going on within. If our cells are repaired while we sleep, then our heart and soul is renewed in the quiet of the alone. And it's there in the stillness that we truly get to know ourselves, learning how to live with genuine inquisitiveness and aspiration, rather than need and escaping.

From day dot I really understood how much I needed alone time, I always understood that I am nowhere near my best self unless I have sufficient time by myself. Like meditation, solo moments can be a practice of awareness, providing many of the qualities necessary to awaken mindfulness such as, fallen expectations, vulnerability, independence, self-realisation, acceptance of the unknown and presence in the here and now. Time alone can feel like a daunting task to take on, but the benefits are numerous and rich.

It supports self-love
Quality time by yourself is the foundation for a healthy relationship with yourself. Alone time allows you to get to know yourself better, to get a real understanding of who you are as a person and discover your authentic self.

It promotes healthy independence
The more time you spend in your own company, the less dependent you are on other people to entertain you, make you happy, to affirm you, or do things for you.

It clears space for perception and intuition
Sure, it's great to have advice and opinions from other people when you're working through challenges. However, all of the answers you will ever need are living inside of you.

It allows you to manifest your dreams
Alone time provides the clear canvas you need to daydream and communicate with the universe about what you want to collaborate on for your future.

CHAPTER EIGHT

ENVIRONMENT

Caring for the environment begins in your home, and that's why everybody can do something to help keep our planet clean! Living a more holistic way of life significantly helps to reduce environmental pollution and reduces toxicity exposure that causes an array of serious health problems. By choosing to embrace a more natural method of cleaning your home, you can eliminate the use of ingredients that are causing allergic reactions to your family and improve everyone's health and immunity."

GREEN CLEANING

The land does not belong to us, we belong to the land."

The smallest change begins in the home; cleaning your home naturally greatly helps to reduce environmental pollution that impacts our waterways and air. Generic cleaning products contain harmful chemicals that are damaging to the skin, eyes, kidneys and lungs. I have put together some of the easiest and most cost-effective ingredients for you to try; most of them can be purchased from the supermarket.

Essential oils – Clove, eucalyptus, lavender, lemon, tea tree, peppermint, and citronella pure essential oils that are highly antibacterial, antifungal, astringent and insect repelling. They also give your home a fresh clean smell and create an uplifting, calm atmosphere.

Essential oil solubiliser – This is a product that allows water and oils to thoroughly combine. It can be used when making cleaning sprays and aromatic room sprays.

Bicarbonate of soda – Sodium bicarbonate, baking soda or bicarb soda acts as a cleaning abrasive and is perfect for the bath, shower, kitchen sink and bathroom floor. It also absorbs odours and acts as a mild disinfectant.

Vegetable glycerine – Vegetable glycerine effectively removes stains from clothes, linen and household materials.

Apple cider vinegar – This is great for cleaning glass and surfaces. It dissolves grease, deodorises and disinfects the whole home. Combined with hot water and pure essential oils, it can be used to mop the floor.

Castile liquid soap – This is an efficient cleanser and is 100 per cent biodegradable. Use it to wash clothes, or as a washing up detergent or hand wash.

Soap powder – Soap powder is an environmentally friendly cleansing agent made from the salts of vegetable fats.

GREEN CLEANING SAFETY

The world is a better place because I give the planet unconditional love and appreciation."

Although natural remedies and pure essential oils are relatively safe, they must be used with understanding and caution.

1. Wear protective gloves as the high concentration of some ingredients may irritate the skin.

2. Label and date all your cleaning products.

3. Keep pure essential oils out of the reach of children; if they are ingested it could be harmful.

4. Do not use undiluted pure essential oils on paint, varnish or plastic surfaces.

5. Follow the safety precautions on the packaging of all ingredients including pure essential oils.

I WENT TO MARKET

"One of the most significant contributions a person can make to the green cause is to choose sustainable foods."

There is something really quite special about giving back to the community whenever and wherever we can by putting money into the pockets of the people who picked, harvested and transported the produce we eat. Some of the best, tastiest and cheapest foods can be found at your local farmers' market. By choosing to buy from supermarkets and neglecting to purchase from smaller businesses and markets you support the mass production industry.

Mass production equals unethical farming and environmental destruction, and because supermarkets control the market price, shopping at supermarkets is the reason why organic produce is more expensive.

Visit WWW.FARMERSMARKETS.ORG.AU to find farmers' markets in your area, and make a family day trip to the nearest one.

To gain a little insight into the destruction of the food industries watch the documentary *Food Inc* by Michael Pollan and Eric Schlosser.

LIVING GREEN

"Organic food is clean, pure, and natural - the way food should be. The word organic implies a holistic view of the farm ecosystem as one cyclic and living being."

Visit one of Australia's leading online resources for locating genuine green businesses, products and services. These sites assist you to find whatever you're looking for that is sustainable and green. Investing in sustainable companies is about investing in the future of your country, health and planet. Make a difference to the world and financially contribute to the companies that care. Change starts with one person; the biggest change comes when we join together and make a difference. You can research organic companies in your city and visit popular online directories. Seek and you shall find.

WWW.THEGREENDIRECTORY.COM.AU
WWW.GREENFINDER.COM.AU
WWW.ORGANICFOODDIRECTORY.COM.AU
WWW.ORGANICFOODMARKETS.COM.AU

MISS EARTH

"We walk for miles trying to find ourselves, when all we have to do is look within."

The biggest problem our environment faces today is, without a doubt, global warming. Burning fossil fuels such as natural gas, coal, oil and gasoline for electricity and transport raises the level of carbon dioxide in the atmosphere. Carbon dioxide is a major contributor to the greenhouse effect and global warming. It is unfortunate that so many people are unaware of what they can do to save our planet; it is either that they somehow feel disconnected from nature, or that they simply don't realise the severity of the global warming issue.

I believe that change starts in our homes, and my passion is to inform others of how to live a more environmentally friendly life. I wish for people to understand that what we do to our planet, we do to ourselves. We can all help to reduce global warming, by using energy more wisely and thinking a little greener. Here are a few tips.

Reduce, reuse, recycle
Do your part to reduce waste by choosing reusable products instead of those that are disposable. Buying products with minimal packaging helps to reduce waste, and whenever you can, recycle paper, plastic, newspaper, glass and aluminium cans. If there isn't a recycling program at your workplace, school, or in your community, ask about starting one. It only takes one person to make a difference.

Always say no to a plastic bag
Bring a hippy cloth or string bag, or reuse plastic bags when you are buying your food and goods. Plastic bags are not biodegradable – even if they say they are they never fully decompose. Also the ink is made up of cadmium, which is highly toxic. Plastic bags are a massive problem, contributing greatly to the pollution of our planet, killing our wildlife and destroying our waterways. Please think before you shop: either say no, or bring your own.

Switch your home electricity to Pure Energy
Simply call Energy Australia and ask about greener options that suit your home and family. Surprisingly it is not expensive. Pure Energy is an easy way to make a difference. By signing up for Pure Energy, you're making a stand every time you flick a switch. That's because, with every flick, you're supporting renewable electricity generation.

I like the bus...
Less driving means fewer emissions. Besides saving money on petrol and parking, walking and biking are great forms of exercise. Explore your community's mass transit system, or check out options for carpooling to work or school. Keep driving to a minimum, and when you do drive, make sure your car is running efficiently.

Buy energy efficient products

Ditch all toxic cleaning and skin products, as these are the things that are destroying the oceans and potentially harming your heath. Get back to basics and feel the difference. Buy environmentally safe cleaning products or make your own using pure essential oils, vinegar and bicarbonate of soda. Switching to organic, synthetic free skincare is one of the best things you can do for your health, including ditching deodorants that contain aluminium. Avoid products that come with excess packaging, that can't be recycled and contain ingredients that are toxic to your body.

Share a shower

Keep your showers short. Set your water heater at 120°C to save energy, and wrap it in an insulating blanket if it is more than five years old. Wash your clothes in warm or cold water to reduce your use of hot water and the energy required to produce it. Use the energy-saving settings on your dishwasher and let the dishes air-dry.

Turn it off

Save electricity and reduce global warming by turning off lights when you leave a room. And remember to turn off your television, video player, stereo and computer when you're not using them. It's also a good idea to turn off the water when you're not using it. While brushing your teeth, shampooing the dog or washing your car, turn off the water until you actually need it for rinsing. You'll reduce your water bill and help to conserve a vital resource.

Plant a tree, man

If you have the means to plant a tree, start digging. During photosynthesis, trees and other plants absorb carbon dioxide and give off oxygen. They are an integral part of the natural atmospheric exchange cycle here on Earth, but there are too few of them to fully counter the increases in carbon dioxide caused by automobile traffic, manufacturing and other human activities. A single tree will absorb approximately one ton of carbon dioxide during its lifetime.

No junk mail please

Put a sign on your letter box or door and say no to flyers, brochures and leaflets that you never read; it's waste! I'm sure that if you saved up all your unwanted junk mail for one year, you would have the equivalent of one and a half trees. Having bank statements and mail sent electronically is very easy, all you have to do is jump online or call up the company and request that all invoices, statements and letters be sent by email.

Encourage others to conserve

Share information about recycling and energy conservation with your friends, neighbours and co-workers, and encourage public officials to establish programs and policies that are good for the environment. People will not think you are a massive hippy if you raise awareness about the environment... In fact this kind of jargon is becoming kinda cool!

SAY NO TO PALM OIL

"Some of us live and act with integrity; these are the people that make a difference to the world."

Palm oil is responsible for the destruction of rainforests and the slaughter of wildlife. Orang-utans are directly affected when palm oil is purchased because each day in many parts of the world, forests are being burned down and palm oil trees are being planted. Palm oil plantations are very lucrative businesses as the oil produced is cheap and used in many packaged and canned foods, soaps, shampoos and make-up. As a direct result of forest destruction, thousands of orang-utans die each year. Deforestation is a major contributor to global warming, and palm oil production is the largest reason for deforestation in Indonesia. Boycotting palm oil is one of the most immediate ways of reducing carbon emissions. Read the labels of foods and cosmetics and if they contain palm oil, please do not buy the product.

Help today and visit
WWW.SAVETHEORANGUTAN.CO.UK
WWW.PALMOILACTION.ORG.AU

NATURE'S EXTERMINATORS

"Everything has its place; every living thing deserves to be here. We all serve a purpose."

Today, preventing the occurrence of insects in your home does not have to be hazardous. Deter unwanted creepy crawlies by using natural methods that ensure your home is free from spiders, dust mites, ticks and cockroaches without harming the environment or killing the creepy crawlies that may be unwanted in your household, but are needed in the ecosystem.

Buzz off
Citronella oil has been effectively deterring mosquitoes, flies and cockroaches for hundreds of years. Sprinkle the undiluted pure essential oil over floorboards and surfaces as often as needed. Make your body and room insect repellent by filling an empty 125ml bottle with purified water and adding 10 drops of citronella, 8 drops of lemongrass and 6 drops of eucalyptus pure essential oil. Add a dash of vodka, or pure distilled alcohol to preserve your spray. Be sure to shake well before use.

Creepy crawlies
In the presence of persistent ants drop undiluted peppermint pure essential oil over the affected area and watch them flee. Peppermint oil acts as a highly effective repellent to most insects especially ants, fleas and mosquitoes. If you're outdoors apply a dab of the concentrated oil to your skin and clothes. Drop peppermint oil in kitchen cupboards and bench tops, leave for a few minutes then wipe over with a clean cloth. Another method to get rid of ants is to pour black pepper down the ant hole.

Incy wincy spider
Pure essential oils are a natural and effective way to banish a spider infestation. Lemon, lime and orange pure essential oils repel spiders. Drop these citrus oils onto a cloth and wipe over any spider prone areas. Add a few drops of lemon, lime and orange pure essential oils and a squirt of liquid castile soap to a mop and bucket and regularly wash your floors with it.

Coming out of the closet
To eliminate moths that linger deep inside your clothes try hanging a bunch of bay leaves in your closets. Sprinkle 20 drops of undiluted cedar wood and lemongrass pure essential oils onto a couple of cotton balls, wrap the cotton balls in a handkerchief, and hang in storage spaces and place in linen draws.

Louie the fly
We need flies to help build human immunity. They are also a good food source for many reptiles and mammals but they can be rather annoying. Commercial fly sprays contain seriously harmful chemicals that must be avoided at all times. For a natural yet highly effective fly repellent that is bursting with a delightfully fresh aroma, fill an empty 125ml bottle with purified water and add 15 drops of lavender, 10 drops of peppermint and 8 drops of eucalyptus pure essential oils, a dash of vodka or pure distilled alcohol and spray freely onto your skin and throughout your home. Be sure to shake the bottle well before use.

For more info on how to become a good "Eco Person" please check out
WWOOF programs
WWW.WWOOFINTERNATIONAL.ORG

YOUR PLANET

"Think globally and act locally."

Making a difference always starts with the smallest of contributions; do your bit for the environment and your health by using natural ingredients to clean your pad! Regular cleaning products are a mix of toxic petrochemicals and perfumes, all of which pollute our waterways and contribute to destroying our ecosystem. Toxic cleaning products like aerosols, dishwashing detergent, furniture polish, bleach and cleaning sprays jeopardize your health, damage your respiratory system, your eyes, brain, liver, kidneys and skin.

There is no need to use harsh chemicals when cleaning your home. Nature provides us with alternatives that are just as effective, if not better. You can safely clean your toilet and sink using baking soda, vinegar and tea tree oil; polish your timber furniture with beeswax and sandalwood oil; use castor oil and pure lemon essential oil to wash your dishes and clove essential oil for mould problems. There are plenty of recipes on the internet and in books for environmentally-friendly cleaning alternatives. Below is my signature multipurpose spray that contains 100 per cent natural ingredients that clean the toilet, shower, fridge, kitchen and bathroom bench tops, is also a great room spray that eliminates bacteria, insects, mould and smelly odours.

ANTIBACTERIAL CLEANING AND ROOM SPRAY

125ml spray bottle
125ml water
10 drops eucalyptus (Eucalyptus globule) pure essential oil
10 drops tea tree (Melaleuca alternifolia) pure essential oil
10 drops lemon (Citrus Limon) pure essential oil
10 drops clove (Syzygium aromatic) pure essential oil
40 drops essential oil solubiliser

Making the Antibacterial Cleaning and Room Spray is as simple as combining all the ingredients together in the spray bottle and gently shaking. Try your spray out on something really filthy. Lemon absorbs grease, clove kills mould and germs, and tea tree and eucalyptus are antifungal and antibacterial.

NOTES

CHAPTER NINE

HIPPY HANGOUTS

"Where we go and what we do affects who we are and who we become. There is unseen energy which can be felt in the environments in which we put ourselves. It is important to surround yourself with positive people and places that lift your energetic vibration and make you feel safe, well nourished and inspired."

BODY, MIND, LIFE

"If there is no struggle, then there will be no progress."

There is no possible way I could have written this book without the regular practise of yoga and meditation.

Vinyasa yoga integrates asanas (yoga postures) and flowing breath to bring about a transform and balance your body, mind and spirit. This process builds conscious awareness.

Yoga encourages for a connection with your true self. Igniting the internal life force, which is the gateway to creativity, inner peace and deep self-satisfaction. The human body responds to the physically and mentally challenging Vinyasa yoga, encouraging you to feel totally relaxed, aware and focused.

The mind works like a muscle. It needs training, so with regular yoga practice you train your mind to be still and you actually begin to feel more present in your life outside the yoga room.

Body Mind Life
Yoga Centres
WWW.BODYMINDLIFE.COM

TRADITIONAL BALINESE HEALER

"A health and spiritual advisor must be free of toxins so their energetic channels are clear. Without clear channels there can be no connection between the healer and the client."

Bali has a long tradition of Bali Usada, a Balinese healing system, which uses natural herbs and spices, holistic therapies and ancient wisdom to cure physical and mental illness. The Balinese live equally in two worlds, and always strive for balance.

In traditional Balinese healing, the physical, mental and spiritual components of a person are addressed in order to truly heal them. The rich Balinese culture includes a wealth of information on herbal remedies, massage and energy healing. Indonesia produces a wide range of herbal medicines; a popular one is known as Jamu made from turmeric, lime and honey. Jamu means tonic or cure-all and is a popular remedy throughout Indonesia.

For more information visit
Bali Holistic Directory
WWW.BALISPIRIT.COM

NEWTOWN FESTIVAL

"Anything that involves music, food and culture feeds the soul and ignites the spirit."

Newtown Festival is held in Camperdown Memorial Rest Park, Newtown, early November every year, and it rocks! The turnout usually attracts over 80,000 diverse individuals. This phenomenal festival is one of Sydney's largest, eccentric, diverse and creative community music festivals. Expect good music… reggae, rock, soul and jazz. There is sustainable clothing, jewellery and food stalls, too. Be inspired at the writers' tent or simply stroll around sampling the sensational cuisine. They have everything from fresh Spanish paella, home-made organic pies to wholesome Hare Krishna food.

Lie on the grass, dance in the street, do whatever. There is something really special about the heritage and vibration of Newtown, and for me the Newtown Festival celebrates this perfectly. After it's all over, swing by the Courthouse pub for a drink and a good feed. You can become really immersed in the vibe of Newtown. The energy of this day is always amazing.

To check out wicked worldwide festivals visit:
WWW.FESTIVALCHASER.COM

THE KITCHEN

"Let food be your medicine and medicine be your food."

Your body is your temple and it truly matters what you feed it. The kitchen, a truly auspicious location, is the pharmacy that holds the remedies that cure and enhance your wellbeing. Visit kitchens, and invite others to yours as often as possible. Fill your utopia kitchen space with fresh produce, herbs, spices, pure essential oils, comfortable chairs, books, photographs, paintings and anything you find inspiring.

The kitchen is a place to congregate, connect and exchange. A gathering of food, family and friends, the kitchen is indeed the place to celebrate life. The taste, aroma, and nourishment found in the kitchen are the products of creativity. The kitchen is like a stage where the cook creates and the audience applauds. It's a place so delightfully pleasant you'll want to stay forever.

AN ENERGETIC HEALER

"When you are in-line with your spirit, you will continually be energised by your life's work."

Embrace your inner goddess with natural ritual based aromatherapy products, or experience one of the many energetic healing treatments, meditation classes or sacred workshops on offer at the Alyssum Alchemy Clinic.

Alison Gallagher is a qualified energetic healer with a Diploma in Energetic Healing who is registered with the national Energetic Healing Association. She has worked in the aromatherapy industry for many years. She is also a qualified meditation teacher and a member of the Australian Teachers of Meditation Association. In addition to facilitating empowering workshops and meditation classes, Alison offers a range of holistic energy and aromatherapy treatments including reiki and chakra balancing.

Alison Gallagher
Alyssum Alchemy Products and Services
WWW.ALYSSUMALCHEMY.COM.AU

COMMON GROUND CAFÉ

"It is through expressing love that extends beyond our differences that we see into the hearts of others. Only then can we truly find common ground."

When you step inside the Common Ground Café, you step inside another world; a world of exceptional service, deliciously wholesome food and a feeling of indescribable nostalgia. The café depicts an enchanting tree house from an old charming children's book, and I felt much like a child during my time there; content, curious and happy. These guys pretty much make all food from scratch. From the tofu satay sandwich on toasted rice bread, and the baked barramundi with creamy dill tartar to their famous organic wholemeal pancakes with honey and seasonal bananas, and macadamia and apple crumble with natural yoghurt, their food is extraordinary.

The folk who run the café believe and follow the teachings of the Bible, both the Old and New Testaments, in a very real and practical way. They believe that God is good and just, and will judge all men according to their deeds... I have this theory that those who eat clean, real food and have some sort of spiritual foundation, are happier, kinder and connect much better with others. My theory was proven right after visiting the Common Ground Café. The experience was more than simply delightful. Go see for yourselves...

Katoomba
Blue Mountains
Sydney, Australia
WWW.COMMONGROUNDCAFE.COM.AU

SUVERAN

"Let food be your medicine and medicine be your food, as nutrition is always the primary cure."

The Suveran is a kind of café slash shop slash information centre slash cool hangout, which is a seriously good place to go. It's good for health advice, good for cooking classes and good for inexpensive local organic produce. The Suveran attracts a crowd of socially aware people who are seeking to live a healthy life. Founder Pete Melov, a truly passionate man dedicated to helping others, believes in only using fresh, non-toxic and organic wildcrafted, high quality ingredients to create delicious meals that are free from dairy, soy, sugar, gluten, wheat, grains, eggs, and yeast. Pete and the Suveran crew have been serving the community for many years.

Some of the things you will find on the versatile and evolving menu are sprouted pizza; lamb and veggie stew; vegan pies; porridge; slices made with millet, chai seed, raisins, coconut water, maca, currants, liquorice root and ginger; and cocoa and carob slices containing goji berries and cashews. The food is always amazingly healthy and delicious, leaving you feeling alive and well.

The Suveran
244 Oxford Street
Bondi Junction
NSW 2022
WWW.THESUV.ORG

SUNSHINE CAFÉ

"Never stop being inquisitive about life..."

In Kyoto, Japan, it is believed that if you stay off the beaten track you will be sure to come across something unique. Being the inquisitive woman I am, I decided to test this theory and get myself lost... Their belief is more than true. The back streets of Kyoto are the homes of many hidden treasures, farmers' markets, traditional teahouses, and blissful onsen and bath houses. The conclusion of this day was the highlight when by chance I came across a small wholesome establishment I had actually read about the very morning prior to visiting called the Sunshine Café. All the ingredients used here are 100 per cent natural, organic and locally sourced, and although it is not a vegetarian restaurant, they have many vegetarian options. The food greatly met my expectations. I enjoyed a rye and soy flour open tofu vegan sandwich with dill mayonnaise, followed by home-made apple and sweet potato cinnamon cake served with organic tofu ice cream. I washed all of this wholesome goodness down with a house circulation tea.

The atmosphere of Sunshine Café is a humble one, it feels as though you are in someone's home. You can relax and read, listen to their quirky choice of music, sit and enjoy the mellow lighting, or study the endless pages of mouth-watering menu choices.

Sunshine Café (Taiyo Café)
4 Ushinomiya-cho, Yoshida, Sakyo-ku
Kyoto, Japan

PERFECT POTION

"How would you like to feel today?"

Visit a Perfect Potion store and step inside a sanctuary of aromatherapy, organic skincare, and spa treatments. Perfect Potion is a storehouse of sensory delights with a plethora of healing teas, pure essential oil blends and ointments designed specifically to nourish and support your wellbeing.

Perfect Potion is an Australian owned and operated company. The founders Salvatore Battaglia and Carolyn Stubbin had a vision to make Perfect Potion the most sought after experience in the world, and they are successfully doing just that, with concept stores across Australia and Japan. Perfect Potion is certified organic and certified natural, a morally sound business that only uses sustainable and ethically sourced ingredients.

The team at Perfect Potion are exceptional – happy, warm and passionate people, who offer superior customer service and product knowledge. The culture of Perfect Potion is contagious, so much so I made it my mission to work for this unique company and continue to do so...

Perfect Potion
90 Northlink Place
Virginia QLD 4014
WWW.PERFECTPOTION.COM.AU
WWW.PERFECTPOTION.CO.JP

GILI YOGA, COMPLETES GILI TRAWANGAN

"Through the practice of yoga we discover that the happiness of others is an essential part of our own quest for happiness."

As the gentle sea breeze caresses my skin, I can almost feel the Indian Ocean penetrate deep within my heart. On a balmy Gili island afternoon Kate Middleton guides an intimate group through one of the most blissful vinyasa yoga classes I have ever experienced.

Gili Yoga offers daily gentle, yet dynamic classes for beginners and the travelling yoga enthusiast, and is a perfect way to unwind and reconnect to your true self in the magical islands of Indonesia.

Gili Yoga
Gili Trawangan, Indonesia
WWW.GILIYOGA.COM

NOTES

CHAPTER TEN

HOLISTIC DIRECTORY

"The holistic directory includes small and larger businesses that aim to supply ethically and environmentally sound products and services. It is a guide to healthy destinations throughout Australia and beyond. By supporting these types of businesses you too are supporting sustainable methods and practices."

CAFES AND RESTAURANTS

Abdulah's Authentic Lebanese
563 Elizabeth Street,
Corner of Cleveland Street
Surry Hills NSW

African Feeling Café
501 King Street
Newtown NSW

Basil Pizza and Pasta
126 King Street
Newtown NSW

Bliss Organic Garden Café
7 Compton Street
Adelaide SA

Bodhi Restaurant
2 College Street
Sydney NSW

Billy Kwong
Shop 3 355 Crown Street
Surry Hills NSW

Bread & Circus
21 Fountain St
Alexandria NSW

Byron Organic Kitchen
4/5 Byron Street
Byron Bay NSW

Cafe Mint
579 Crown Street
Surry Hills NSW

Common Ground Café
Katoomba
Blue Mountains
Sydney NSW

Commune Espresso
1844 Gold Coast Highway
Burleigh Heads QLD

Day Dreamer's Café
61–71 McIlwrick Street
Windsor Melbourne VIC

Earth Food Store
81 Gould Street
Bondi Beach NSW

Earth To Table
Raw Cafe
WWW.FACEBOOK.COM/PAGES/EARTH-TO-
TABLE

Emon – Natural Japanese
432 Cleveland Street
Surry Hills NSW

Estabar
61 Shortland Esplanade
Newcastle NSW

Fundies Wholefoods Café
219 Given Terrace
Paddington QLD

Funky Pies Café
144-148 Glenayr Avenue
Bondi NSW

Gnostic Forest Corner
31 The Boulevard
Woy Woy NSW

Green Gourmet
Vegan Restaurants
WWW.GREENGOURMET.COM.AU

Green Lizard Vegan and Fusion
Raw Food Café
20/230 William Street
Kings Cross NSW

Hare Krishna
Sri Radha-Gopinath Mandir
180 Falcon Street
North Sydney NSW

Harvest Café
29 Albert Street
Daylesford VIC

Harvest Café
18 Old Pacific Highway
Newrybar Byron Bay
Hinterland NSW

Harvest Vegetarian Restaurant
71 Evans Street
Rozelle NSW

Heart and Soul Organic Chai Café
Cronulla NSW
WWW.HEARTANDSOULCAFE.COM.AU

Himalayan Café
640 Brunswick Street
New Farm QLD

IKU Wholefood Cafés Australia
WWW.IKUWHOLEFOOD.COM

Jivamukti Yoga Sydney
Sadhana Kitchen
76 Wilford Street
Newton NSW

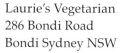

Kammadhenu
Sri Lankan
171 King Street
Newtown NSW

Laurie's Vegetarian
286 Bondi Road
Bondi Sydney NSW

Love Grub
38 Mitchell Road
Alexandria NSW

Madam Char Char
285A Crown Street
Surry Hills NSW

Magic Apple Café
Gold Coast Highway
and 5th Avenue
Burleigh Heads
Gold Coast QLD

Miss Chu
Vietnamese
1/150 Bourke Street
Darlinghurst NSW

Mondo Organics Restaurant
166 Hardgrave Road
West End QLD

Moroccan Soup Bar
183 St Georges Road
Fitzroy North VIC

Nature Care Café
Nature Care College
46 Nicholson Street
St Leonards NSW

Nourishing Quarter
315 Cleveland Street,
Redfern NSW

Oneness Cafe Restaurant
244 Coogee Bay Road
Coogee NSW

Organic Produce Café
487 Crown Street
Surry Hills NSW

Organic Republic Bakery
98/100 Glenayr Avenue
Bondi Beach NSW

Pink Peppercorn
Laotian and Burmese
122 Oxford Street
Darlinghurst NSW

Pure Wholefoods
Shop 5, 10 Darley Road
Manly NSW

Raw Café
33 Hunter Street
Newcastle NSW

Ritual Restaurant
Shop 1 & 2 Austral Street
Shopping Village
Nelson Bay NSW

Roberts Restaurant
Hunter Valley
WWW.ROBERTSCIRCA1876.COM

Sean's Panaroma
270 Campbell Parade
Bondi NSW

Soul Cake Café
23 Broken Bay Road
Ettalong Beach NSW

Sourced Café and Grocer
11 Florence Street
Teneriffe QLD

Speak Easy Bar and Café
83 Curlewis Street
Bondi Beach NSW

Suveran Café
244 Oxford Street
Bondi Junction NSW

The Banyan Tree
39 Beaumont Street
Hamilton NSW

The Book Kitchen
255 Devonshire Street
Surry Hills NSW

The Grounds of Alexandria
Building 7a, no.2 Huntley St
Alexandria NSW

The Lansdowne Cafe
68 Lansdowne Crescent
Hobart TAS

The Orange Banana Shop
Shop 3-4/78 York Street
East Gosford NSW

The Organic Food and Wine Deli
28 Degraves St
Melbourne VIC

The Organic Pomegranate
534 King Street
Newtown NSW

The Peasants' Feast Restaurant
121A King Street
Newtown NSW

The Raw Kitchen
Freemantle WA
WWW.THERAWKITCHEN.COM.AU

The Vegie Bar
380 Brunswick Street
Melbourne VIC

Urban Food Store and Cafe
Edinburgh Avenue
Canberra ACT
Vege Rama
Shop 1, 300 Queen Street Building
Brisbane QLD

Wafu – Organic Japanese Cuisine
460 Cleveland Street
Surry Hills NSW

SHOPS

About Life – Marketplace
605 Darling Street Rozelle
Sydney NSW

And 31–37 Oxford Street
Bondi Junction
Sydney NSW

Affordable Organics
96 Arthur Street
Magill SA

Alfalfa House
113 Enmore Road
Newtown NSW

Blue Mountains Co-op
Shops 1 and 2 Jones House

Ha'penny Lane
Katoomba NSW

Doctor Earth, Go Vita
444 Oxford Street
Bondi Junction NSW

Great Earth
90 Elizabeth Street
Melbourne VIC

Greenhouse Emporium
277 Canberra Avenue
Fyshwick ACT

Grub
Grass Roots Urban Butchery
101 New South Head Road
Vaucluse NSW

Habib Wholefoods
260 Flinders Street
Melbourne VIC

Hand 'n' Hoe
Organic Macadamias
900 Kippax Road
Wingham NSW

Herbies Spices
745 Darling Street
Rozelle NSW

Lemongrass House
114 King Street
Newtown NSW

Manna Wholefoods
274 South Terrace
South Fremantle WA

Naturally Gluten-free
1/373 Mann's Road
West Gosford NSW

Newton's Pharmacy
119 York Street
Sydney NSW

Raw - The Natural Food Store
118 King Street
Sandy Bay TAS

Ripe Organics Prahran
Shop 7
Prahran Market
Prahran VIC

Spellbox
Shop 17 Royal Arcade
Bourke Street Mall
Melbourne VIC

Sun and Earth Organics
845 Brunswick Street
New Farm QLD

Tamburlaine Vineyards
Organic Vineyard
Pokolbin NSW
WWW.TAMBURLAINE.COM.AU

The Health Emporium
263–265 Bondi Road
Bondi NSW

The Tea Centre
Speciality Tea Shops
WWW.THETEACENTRE.COM.AU

Thoughtful Foods Co-op
Roundhouse
University of New South Wales
Sydney NSW

Wholefoods House
109 Queen Street
Woollahra NSW

EVENTS AND FESTIVALS

Bali Spirit Festival
Bali Indonesia
WWW.BALISPIRITFESTIVAL.COM
Annually

Bellingen Global Carnival
Bellingen NSW
WWW.GLOBALCARNIVAL.COM
Annually

Clean up Australia Day
WWW.CLEANUP.ORG.AU
Annually

Green Earth Day
WWW.GREENEARTHDAY.NET
Annually

National Recycling Week
WWW.RECYCLINGWEEK.PLANETARK.ORG
Annually

Newtown Festival
Sydney NSW
WWW.NEWTOWNCENTRE.ORG
Annually

Organic Expo and Green Show
WWW.ORGANICEXPO.COM.AU
Annually

Peats Ridge Sustainable Arts and
Music Festival
Glenworth Valley NSW
WWW.PEATSRIDGEFESTIVAL.COM.AU
Annually 29th December – 1st of January

ONLINE

Sustain Festival
Sydney NSW
WWW.ORGANICEXPO.COM.AU
Annually

The Festival of Tibet
Brisbane Powerhouse
WWW.BRISBANEPOWERHOUSE.ORG
Annually

Ubud Writers' Festival
Bali Indonesia
WWW.UBUDWRITERSFESTIVAL.COM
Annually

Vegan Festival Adelaide
South Australia
WWW.VEGANFESTIVAL.INFO
Annually

Winter Magic Festival
Katoomba
Blue Mountains NSW
WWW.WINTERMAGIC.COM.AU
Annually

WOMAD Festival
Adelaide SA
WWW.WOMADELAIDE.COM.AU
Annually

Woodford Folk Festival
QLD Australia
WWW.WOODFORDFOLKFESTIVAL.COM
Annually

Yoga Aid World Challenge
Sydney NSW
WWW.YOGAAID.COM
Annually

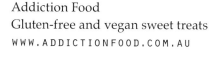

Addiction Food
Gluten-free and vegan sweet treats
WWW.ADDICTIONFOOD.COM.AU

Alter Eco
Fair trade
WWW.ALTERECOPACIFIC.COM

Amazonia
Certified Organic
Acai Berry Products
WWW.PURPLEBERRY.COM.AU

Angove
Organic Winemakers
WWW.ANGOVE.COM.AU

Arthur Avenue
Sustainable Fashion Label
WWW.ARTHURAVE.COM.AU

Aussie Farmers Direct
Online Home Delivery Service
WWW.AUSSIEFARMERS.COM.AU

Australian Farmers Markets Association
WWW.FARMERSMARKETS.ORG.AU

Australian Organic Food Directory
Organic produce and products
WWW.ORGANICFOODDIRECTORY.COM.AU

Bali Holistic Directory
WWW.BALISPIRIT.COM

Body and Soul
WWW.BODYANDSOUL.COM.AU

BsaB
Natural soy and beeswax candles
WWW.BSABCANDLES.COM

Cams Community Organics
Sydney Organic Fresh Produce
Home Delivery
WWW.CAMSCOMMUNITYORGANICS.COM

Canaan Fair Trade Products
WWW.CANAANFAIRTRADE.COM

Choices
Gluten and wheat free products
WWW.CHOICESGLUTENFREE.COM.AU

Cocopure
Coconut Super Foods
WWW.COCOPURE.COM.AU

Co Yo
Gourmet Coconut Yoghurts
WWW.COYO.COM.AU

David Wolfe
Health Expert
WWW.DAVIDWOLFE.COM

Earth Choice
Cleaning Products
WWW.NATURESORGANICS.COM.AU

Eat Fit Food
Prepared and Delivered Meals
WWW.EATFITFOOD.COM.AU

Eco Directory
Australia's guide to sustainable living
WWW.ECODIRECTORY.COM.AU

Eco Friendly Weddings
WWW.ECOFRIENDLYWEDDINGS.COM.AU

Eden Organics
Organic Produce and Products
WWW.EDENFOODS.COM

Elephant Journal
Yoga, sustainability, politics and
spirituality
WWW.ELEPHANTJOURNAL.COM

Emma and Tom's Juices and Health Bars
WWW.EMMAANDTOM.COM

Faye De Lanty
Fashion Hound
WWW.FASHIONHOUND.TV.

Found
Organic Juice
WWW.FOUNDORGANIC.COM.AU

Fusion Health
TCM Vitamins
WWW.FUSIONHEALTH.COM.AU

Golden Body Foods
High vibration foods
WWW.GOLDENBODYFOODS.COM

Green and Blacks
Organic chocolate
WWW.GREENANDBLACKS.COM

Green Lifestyle
Simple Sustainable Living
WWW.GMAGAZINE.COM.AU

Grow It Local
Your Local Grow Community
WWW.GROWITLOCAL.COM.AU

Happy Cow
Compassionate eating guide
WWW.HAPPYCOW.NET

Happy High Herbs
Herbs and herbal paraphernalia
WWW.HAPPYHIGHHERBS.COM

Healthelicious Foods
Organic Produce and Products
WWW.HEALTHELICIOUS.COM.AU

His Holiness the Dalai Lama
Official website
WWW.DALAILAMA.COM

Homemade Food
Food, Products and Services Directory
WWW.HOMEMADEFOOD.COM.AU

Honest To Goodness
Organic produce and products
WWW.GOODNESS.COM.AU

Kasia Sierzant
Wands of Transformation
HTTP://ON.FB.ME/WANDS-OF-
TRANSFORMATION

Kitsa's Kichen
Organic Produce and Products
WWW.KITSASKITCHEN.COM

Kitz Living Foods
Organic Produce and Products
WWW.KITZLIVINGFOODS.COM.AU

Loving Earth
Raw Chocolate
WWW.LOVINGEARTH.NET

Mary's Gone Crackers
Organic produce and products
WWW.MARYSGONECRACKERS.COM

Melrose – The Whole Body Health Co.
Organic Produce and Products
WWW.MELROSEHEALTH.COM.AU

Metagenics
Practitioner grade vitamins
WWW.METAGENICS.COM.AU

Mimi Elashiry Creative Space
WWW.MIMIELASHIRY.COM

Mojo Kombucha
Raw Drinks
WWW.ORGANICANDRAW.COM.AU

Natural News
WWW.NATURALNEWS.COM

Natural Weddings
WWW.NATURALWEDDINGS.COM.AU

Neisha Smith
Ethically produced clothing
WWW.NEISHACLOTHING.COM

Noah's Creative Juices
WWW.NOAHSJUICE.COM.AU

Nova Australia's Holistic Journal
WWW.NOVAMAGAZINE.COM.AU

Nushie's Natural
Organic Produce and Products
WWW.NUSHIESNATURAL.COM.AU

Olive Oil
Soap Company
WWW.OLIVEOILSKINCARE.COM.AU

Orchid Street
Juice Cleanse
WW.ORCHARDSTREET.COM.AU

Organic Food Markets
WWW.ORGANICFOODANDFARMERSMARKETS.
COM.AU

249

Organic Plant Doctor
WWW.PLANTDOCTOR.COM.AU

Organic Road
Organic Produce and Products
WWW.ORGANICROAD.COM.AU

Oxfam Australia
Sustainable and Humanitarian Products
WWW.OXFAM.ORG.AU

Oxfam Unwrapped
Charity Christmas Gifts
WWW.OXFAMUNWRAPPED.COM.AU

Pana Chocolate
Organic Chocolate
WWW.PANACHOCALATE.COM

People Tree
Fair trade fashion and accessories
WWW.PEOPLETREE.CO.UK

Planet Organic
Organic Produce and Products
WWW.PLANETORGANIC.COM.AU

Pure Earth Wines
Organic Vineyard
Hunter Valley NSW
WWW.PUREEARTHWINES.COM

Raw Enerqi
Raw Food Catering
WWW.RAWENERQI.COM

Rawganic
Raw Chocolate
WWW.RAWGANIC.COM.AU

Raw Revolution
Organic Live Food Bars
WWW.RAWINDULGENCE.COM

Spirit of Woman
Australian Wild Flower Essences
WWW.SPIRITOFWOMANESSENCES.COM

Sydney Spiritual Enquirer
WWW.SPIRITUALENQUIRER.BLOGSPOT.
COM

The Art of Eating
Nutrition and dietary training
WWW.THEARTOFEATING.COM.AU

The Gorgeous Vegetarian
Health, Beauty, Food For Thought
WWW.THEGORGEOUSVEGETARIAN.COM.AU

The Saved Planet
Green Services Directory
WWW.THESAVEDPLANET.COM.AU

The Veggie Patch
Sustainable Pop-Up Restaurant
WWW.VEGGIEPATCHVAN.COM.AU

Thrive Natural Foods
Cooking Classes and Products
WWW.THRIVEFOODS.COM.AU

Wellbeing Magazine
WWW.WELLBEING.COM.AU

Wellbeing For Dogs
Natural Pet Foods
WWW.WELLBEINGFORDOGS.COM.AU

Wholefood Cooking
Natural Chef Training
WWW.WHOLEFOODCOOKING.COM.AU

Wild Fox Wines
Organic wines
WWW.WILDFOXWINES.COM

WSPA Animal Rescue
WWW.WSPA.ORG.AU

Yoga Journal
WWW.YOGAJOURNAL.COM.AU

YOGA, MEDITATION AND RETREAT

Body, Mind, Life
Yoga classes
WWW.BODYMINDLIFE.COM

Breathe
Yoga and Pilates
Melbourne VIC
WWW.BREATHEWELLBEING.COM.AU

Como Shambhala
WWW.COMOSHAMBHALA.COMO.BZ

Daintree Eco Lodge and Spa
WWW.DAINTREE-ECOLODGE.COM.AU

Desa Seni
Canggu Bali
WWW.DESASENI.COM

Emily Odillo Maher
Yoga teacher
WWW.BLISSEDOUT.COM.AU

Find Yoga
Yoga directory
WWW.FINDYOGA.COM.AU

Govinda Valley
Spiritual Retreat Centre
Otford NSW
WWW.GOVINDAVALLEY.COM.AU

Gili Yoga
Gili Trawangan
Lombok Indonesia
WWW.GILIYOGA.COM

Jasper's Village Resort
Yoga retreat
WWW.JASPERSPEAK.COM.AU

Kate Kendall
Yoga master
WWW.ELEVATEEVENTS.COM.AU

Kate Pippos
Yoga teacher
WWW.LOVESPIRITYOGA.COM

Kelli Angela Prieur
Yoga teacher
KELLISHEARTGLOW.BLOGSPOT.COM

KMYOGA
Bondi Junction NSW
WWW.KMYOGA.COM

Lulu Lululemon
Everything Yoga
WWW.LULULEMON.COM

Mahasiddha Kadampa
Meditation Centre
WWW.MEDITATEINSYDNEY.ORG

Meditasi Bungalows
Amed Bali
HTTP://MEDITASI.8M.COM

Murray Hatton
Yoga teacher and trainer
WWW.BODYMINDLIFE.COM

Persia Rutchinski
Yoga teacher
WWW.BODYMINDLIFE.COM

Samudra Shala
Yoga, Surf and Food for Life
Western Australia
WWW.SAMUDRA.COM.AU

Satyananda
Yoga Retreats
WWW.SATYANANDA.NET

Soul Shine Villa & Retreat Centre
Ubud, Bali
WWW.SOULSHINEBALI.COM

Sukha Mukha
Yoga Studio
Bronte NSW
WWW.SUKHAMUKHA.COM

Swasti Eco Cottages
Ubud Bali
WWW.BALISWASTI.COM

Sydney Gay Meditation Group
99 Crown Street
Sydney NSW
WWW.SYDNEYGAYMEDITATIONGROUP.COM

The Divine Centre
152 Victoria Road
Bellevue Hill NSW
WWW.PURPLEBERRY.COM.AU

The Future Sound of Yoga
WWW.FUTURESOUNDOFYOGA.COM

The Living Room
Yoga studio
Coogee NSW
WWW.THELIVINGROOMCOOGEE.COM.AU

NATURAL SKINCARE

Blue Stone Botanicals
Natural skincare and aromatherapy
WWW.BLUESTONEBOTANICALS.COM

Carla Oates
Natural skincare
WWW.CARLAOATESBEAUTY.COM

Dr Hauschka
Natural skincare and make-up
WWW.DRHAUSCHKA.COM.AU

Gaia Skin Naturals
Natural skincare
WWW.GAIASKINNATURALS.COM

Inika
Natural cosmetics
WWW.INIKA.COM.AU

INTERNATIONAL

Kora organics
Natural skincare
WWW.KORAORGANICS.COM

Lavera
Natural skincare and make-up
WWW.LAVERA.COM

Miessence
Natural skincare and make-up
WWW.INESSENCE-ORGANICS.COM

Neal's Yard Remedies
Natural skincare and remedies
WWW.NEALSYARDREMEDIES.COM

Nude by nature
Natural make-up
WWW.NUDEBYNATURE.COM.AU

Perfect Potion
Aromatherapy products
WWW.PERFECTPOTION.COM.AU
WWW.PERFECTPOTION.COM.JP

Sukin
Natural skincare
WWW.SUKINORGANICS.COM

Tinderbox
Natural skincare and herbal remedies
WWW.CHEEKYHERBS.COM

Utama Spice
Natural skincare and herb walk tours
Ubud Bali
WWW.UTAMASPICEBALI.COM

Vanessa Megan
Natural skincare
WWW.VANESSAMEGAN.COM

Alchemy
Jalan Penestanan
Ubud Bali
WWW.ALCHEMYBALI.COM

Bali Buddha Café
Ubud Bali
WWW.BALIBUDDHA.BIZ

Bliss Café
Brooklyn New York
11211 40.717521 -73.958 nr. N. 7th St

Blossom
New York
WWW.BLOSSOMNYC.COM

Bright Earth Foods
Natural super foods
WWW.BRIGHTEARTHFOODS.COM

Cafe Gratitude
San Francisco
WWW.CAFEGRATITUDE.COM

Candle Cafe
New York
WWW.CANDLECAFE.COM

Clear Café
Ubud Bali
WWW.CLEAR-CAFE-UBUD.COM

Down To Earth
Seminyak Bali
WWW.DOWNTOEARTHBALI.COM

Euphoria Loves Rawvolution
Santa Monica California
WWW.EUPHORIALOVESRAWVOLUTION.COM

Friends Café
Phnom Penh Cambodia
WWW.STREETFRIENDS.ORG

Greens Restaurant
San Francisco
WWW.GREENSRESTAURANT.COM

Kafe Café
Ubud Bali
WWW.BALISPIRIT.COM/KAFE

Life Food Organic
Los Angeles California
WWW.LIFEFOODORGANIC.COM

Marco Inn Jalan Segara
Padang Bai Bali
WWW.BALIFROMHOME.COM

Mr Ketut Liyer
Medicine Man
Pengosekan-Mas
Ubud Bali

Perfect Potion
Aromatherapy Café
Kyoto Japan
WWW.PERFECTPOTION.CO.JP

Raw World Restaurants
Raw café directory
WWW.GORAWCAFE.COM

Río Muchacho Organic Farm
Manabi Ecuador
WWW.RIOMUCHACHO.COM

Sari Organik Café
Organic café and farm
Ubud Bali

Soma – High Vibe Organic Delights
Raw vegan café
Ubud Bali
WWW.SOMABALI.COM

Sunshine Café (Taiyo Café)
4 Ushinomiya-cho,
Yoshida, Sakyo-ku
Kyoto Japan

Ubuntu Restaurant and Yoga Studio
Napa California
WWW.UBUNTUNAPA.COM

Veggie Hotels
WWW.VEGGIE-HOTELS.COM

Warung Alami
Jalan Penestanan
Ubud Bali
WWW.WARUNGALAMI.JIMDO.COM

Warung Murah
Chinese Indonesian Natural Food
Jl. Double Six No. 99
Kuta Bali

Whole Foods Market
Union Square New York
WWW.WHOLEFOODSMARKET.COM

Yellow Flower Café
Ubud Bali
WWW.YELLOWFLOWERCAFE.COM

PRACTITIONERS AND THERAPY

Andrijana Miler
Massage therapist
and intuitive healer
amiler@hotmail.com

Back2health
Multi Modality Health Centre
West End QLD
WWW.BACK2HEALTH.NET.AU

Carmen Fearnley
Aromatherapist
WWW.THEPURITYPROMISE.COM

Carol Man
Ayurvedic lifestyle consultant/therapist
Yoga teacher
WWW.AYUESSENCE.COM

Crystal Breedon
Reiki
inscented@gmail.com

Dr Marilyn Golden
Doctor and Naturopath
WWW.MARILYNGOLDEN.COM.AU

Dr Robert
Traditional Chinese Medicine
75-77 Ultimo Road
Sydney NSW

Dr Tsering Thakchoe Drungtso
Traditional Tibetan doctor
WWW.TIBMEDCOUNCIL.ORG

Ester Van der Sande
Life coach
0424 622 914
WWW.GOLIFECOACHING.COM.AU

Fumi Yamamoto
Yoga and wellness consultant
WWW.ZENFACIAL.COM

Indira Geisbuhl
Massage therapist
Indiram226@hotmail.com

Jack Marshall
Zen Shiatsu therapist
Uclinic Level 1/421 Bourke Street
Surry Hills NSW

Jade Gluckman
Awareness Therapy
WWW.JADEGLUCKMAN.COM

Jake Zakarauskas
Counselling and psychotherapy
WWW.THERAPYWITHJAKE.COM

Janella Purcell
Naturopath, nutritionist,
herbalist and iridologist
WWW.JANELLAPURCELL.COM

Jen Brown
Soul and past life coach
WWW.YOURSOULCOACH.COM.AU

Jo Mulcahy
Naturopath
jomulcahy@hotmail.com

Kathleen Gaffney
Zen Shiatsu therapist
Gerringong seaview shiatsu
0422 072 536

Kellie Wood
Naturopathic nutritionist
Holistic Kinesiologist
WWW.CENTREDLIVING.COM.AU

Kristina Luke
Kinesiology
kristinaluke05@gmail.com

Melissa Ambrosini
Holistic health and life coach
WWW.PATHTOWELLNESS.COM.AU

EDUCATION

Michael Solano
Eastern Suburbs Osteopathy
WWW.ESOSTEOPATHY.COM.AU

Michelle Terry
Massage therapist
Reiki practitioner
chellefelt@gmail.com

Miriam White
Personal trainer
info@seefit.com.au

Sarah Baiada
Massage therapist,
nutritionist and spiritual healer
s_baiada@hotmail.com

Sarah O'Callaghan
Aromatherapist
shackosaz@hotmail.com

Suki Zoe
Colonic irrigation therapist
me@sukizoe.com

Vivienne Grey
Reiki
WWW.JEREMIA.COM.AU

Australasian College of Natural Therapies
WWW.ACNT.EDU.AU

Australian Institute of Applied Sciences
WWW.AIAS.COM.AU

Endeavour College of Natural Health
WWW.ENDEAVOUR.EDU.AU

Institute for Integrative Nutrition
WWW.INTEGRATIVENUTRITION.COM

International College of Wellness Coaches
WWW.ICWC.COM.AU

Nature Care College
WWW.NATURESCARE.COM.AU

Southern School of Natural Therapies
WWW.SSNT.EDU.AU

Phoenix Distribution
WWW.PHOENIXDISTRIBUTION.COM.AU

GLOSSARY

Alkaline – Alkaline means a substance that has a pH of more than seven.

Amino Acids – Are the building blocks of proteins. The chemical properties of the amino acids of proteins will determine the biological activity of the protein.

Antibacterial – Inhibits the growth of harmful bacteria in the body.

Anti-inflammatory – Is something that re-duces inflammation in the body internally and externally.

Antiseptic – Prevents the growth of various bacteria and micro-organisms.

Antioxidants – Are molecules capable of inhibiting the oxidation of other molecules. Antioxidants are naturally occurring chemicals in foods that help to counter the negative effects of free radicals.

Ayurvedic Medicine – Also called Ayurveda, this system of medicine that originated and evolved in India, and is one of the world's oldest healthcare systems.

B Vitamins – There are eight B-group vitamins, which are essential for human bodily functions such as energy production. B vitamins are a group of water-soluble vitamins that play an important role in cell metabolism.

Baking Soda – Also known as bicarbonate of soda and sodium bicarbonate, is a natu-ral chemical salt widely used for cooking, cleaning and medicinal purposes.

Beta-Carotene – Is a substance found in plants, especially carrots and colourful vegetables. The body converts beta-carotene into vitamin A which is needed for good vision, a strong immune system, and healthy skin.

Biodynamic – Is a form of organic farming that actively works to support the environment. The farming methods used are aligned with the rhythms of nature.

Calcium – Is an element and is vital to optimum health, playing critical roles in strengthening bones and teeth, regulating muscle and heart function.

Citrus Seed Extract – Also known as grapefruit seed extract, this is a liquid derived from the seeds, pulp and membranes of the grapefruit. The extract is a widely used alternative medicine that contains antibacterial, antiviral, and antifungal properties. It is also used to alleviate diarrhoea.

Colonic Irrigation – Colon hydrotherapy, also known as a colonic, is an alternative medicine practice that involves flushing the colon with warm purified water. Colonic irrigation removes a build up of waste maintaining the health of the digestive tract.

Essential Fatty Acids – Are fatty acids that are needed for good health and because the human body cannot synthesise them essential fatty acids must be obtained through food.

Essential Oils – An essential oil is a concentrated liquid containing volatile aroma compounds from plants. Essential oils are also known as volatile oils, ethereal oils or aetherolea. They are commonly named after the plant from which they are extracted. Various essential oils have been used medicinally at different periods in history.

Exfoliation – Using a skincare product with an abrasive texture to remove the surface layer of dead skin cells. Exfoliation is beneficial for promoting cell renewal and soft skin.

Free-range – Is a term that may apply to meat, eggs or dairy farming. It describes a method of farming where the animals are allowed to roam freely instead of being contained.

GMO-free – Are foods that have not been genetically modified or engineered.

Green Clay – One of the most common forms of green clay is Bentonite, an Aluminium Silicate smectite. Clays have traditionally been used for internal detoxification and treating skin conditions. Quality French and Australian clays are mined and dried in the sun. Green, white, red, pink, and yellow clay and kaolin are all good for skincare treatments.

Gluten Intolerance – The two primary forms of gluten intolerance are coeliac disease and non-coeliac gluten sensitivity. Symptoms of gluten sensitivity include bloating, joint pain, abdominal discomfort. It may present with a variety of symptoms including headaches, lethargy and a variety of intestinal issues.

Holistic Nutrition – Focuses on the therapeutic value of wholefoods and environmental influences on a person's wellbeing, aiming to achieve optimal health and wellbeing.

Insoluble fibre – There are two types of fibre, soluble and insoluble. Insoluble fibre does not break down as it passes through the digestive tract, helping to bulk up stools and encourage regular bowel movements.

Iodine – Iodine is a non-metallic chemical element important for hormone development which is necessary for regulating your body's growth, development, body temperature and metabolism.

Iron – Is a chemical element and mineral that is a available in two forms, haem and non-haem. Iron is needed for various bodily functions, including the transport of oxygen in the blood.

Maca – Maca (Lepidium meyenii) is a root that has long been used as a food and for medicinal purposes.

Magnesium – Is a mineral and chemical element with many important roles within the body. It is essential for the effective functioning of the nerves and muscles, and also helps build and strengthen bones.

Melatonin – Is a naturally occurring hormone that is helpful in treating some sleep problems including insomnia.

Metabolism – Is the set of chemical reactions that occur in the cells of living organisms. The chemical reactions of metabolism are organised into metabolic pathways.

Minerals – A mineral is a naturally occurring chemical substance that is formed through biochemical processes. Like vitamins, minerals help boost the immune system, and support cell and organ function.

Natural – A term used to describe substances that exist in nature that have not been processed or engineered. The term "natural" is often used loosely in skincare and cosmetics. A product may contain a few natural ingredients and many synthetic ingredients, yet the product is still called natural; in these cases the product is not wholly of plant origin.

Organic – Scientifically organic means a substance that contains carbon atoms. It's a term used to describe produce that has been developed or grown without the use of synthetic pesticides or fertilisers.

pH – Refers to the level of acidity or alkalinity of a substance. The normal pH level of the skin ranges from around 5.5 to 6.5.

Pectin – Pectin is a natural thickening agent found in fruits and vegetables. It is commonly used to gel jams, but is also used in medications and cosmetics. It is most often derived from apple and orange peels, and can be purchased in both powder and liquid form.

Pesticide-free – Ideally it means no chemical pesticides, including synthetic petrochemical-based insecticides that have been used on produce.

Phosphorus – A dietary mineral that is important to many bodily functions such as bone development, energy production and healthy cell membranes.

Potassium – The chemical element potassium is a very important mineral for the proper function of all cells, tissues, and organs in the body.

Proteins – Proteins are made up of units called amino acids, which are attached to one another in long chains. Proteins play a crucial role in the body. They are required for the function and regulation of the body's tissues and organs.

Preservatives – Chemical compounds that are added to products to protect and preserve them against decomposition. Vitamin E and ascorbic acid are both natural preservatives.

Sustainable Farming Methods – Also known as sustainable agriculture, is the practice of farming using principles of ecology that support environmental health.

Traditional Chinese Medicine (TCM) – An ancient holistic system of health and healing, which is based on the notion of harmony and balance. TCM employs practices of acupuncture, massage, lifestyle advice and more. The structure is based around prevention and moderation.

Traditional Tibetan Medicine – Is an ancient medical system that employs a complex approach to diagnosis. Tibetan medicines take various forms, from decoctions, dietary adjustments, herbs and natural methods of treatment. The Tibetan medical system is based upon a fusion of the Indian, Persian, Greek and Chinese medical systems.

Turmeric – A root that is part of the ginger family, commonly used as a spice in curries and other South Asian and Middle Eastern cuisine. Usually used in its dried, powdered form, turmeric is also used fresh, much like ginger.

Vitamins – A group of organic compounds needed for optimum health. Vitamins are essential nutrients found in many food sources.

Vitamin C – This is a water-soluble vitamin and antioxidant that has a number of biological functions. Vitamin C is required for the growth and repair of tissues in all parts of the body. It helps make collagen and protects the immunity system.

Wheat Allergy – Wheat allergy is a food allergy and people with a wheat allergy have an abnormal immune system response to the proteins that exist in wheat.

Wildcrafted – This means that the plants are carefully collected from their unspoiled natural habitat. Ethical considerations are implemented, such as protecting endangered species.

Zinc – This essential mineral is a component of more than 300 enzymes needed to repair wounds, boost immunity, promote fertility. It is an important requirement for growth and development in children.

Basil – Botanical name Osmium basilica. Basil has a sweet and herbaceous aroma, best used during the day as it greatly stimulates the mind and sharpen the senses.

Bergamot – Botanical name Citrus bergamia. Bergamot has an uplifting and joyful citrus scent that is used to treat depression, stress, tension, and anxiety. It is also useful for treating infection and herpes viruses.

Black Pepper – Botanical name Piper nigrum. Black pepper has a warm, soothing, spicy scent that is strengthening, uplifting and energising. Black pepper oil can be used for increasing circulation and for sore tired muscles.

Cedarwood – Botanical name Cedrus atlantica. Cedarwood has a sweet woody aroma which is perfect for binding masculine perfume blends. It is good for acne, nervous tension, coughs and colds. It is also an aphrodisiac.

German Chamomile – Botanical name Matricaria recutita and **Roman Chamomile** – Botanical name Chamaemelum nobilis. Both chamomiles are used to calm nervous tension, treat digestive disorders and relieve muscle spasms. Both contain calming anti-inflammatory properties to soothe skin conditions such as eczema and psoriasis.

Cinnamon – Botanical name Cinnamomum zeylanicum. It has a spicy, warm, rich aroma. The many health benefits of cinnamon can be attributed to its antibacterial, antifungal, anti-microbial and anti-clotting properties.

Clary sage – Botanical name Salvia sclarea. The odour of clary sage is quite distinct, and the herb has many soothing properties which are beneficial for relaxation and overcoming stress. Pregnant women, however, should avoid exposure to clary sage, because it may induce contractions.

Clove – Botanical name Syzygium aromaticum. Clove oil has a sweet and spicy scent creating a warm and cosy environment. Western studies have supported the use of cloves and clove oil for toothaches.

Cypress – Botanical name Cupressus sempervirens. Cypress has a fresh and herbaceous scent that leaves you feeling refreshed. Cypress is also useful for lymphatic congestion, rheumatic pain, reducing cellulite and strengthening the circulatory system.

Eucalyptus – Botanical name Eucalyptus globules. There are around 300 different varieties of eucalyptus. Eucalyptus has a fresh and invigorating aroma and is best known for its decongestant properties, making it an ideal treatment for colds, flu and sinusitis.

Fennel – Botanical name Foeniculum vulgare. Fennel has a sweet, peppery, somewhat spicy and liquorice-like aroma. Fennel is used to treat cellulite, flatulence, nausea and fluid retention. It also has a soothing effect on the digestive system.

Frankincense – Botanical name Boswellia carteri. Having a somewhat fresh and balsamic odour, frankincense is known to calm and soothe the whole body and mind. It eases aches and pains, heals wounds, clears the lungs and acts as a skin tonic and anti-ageing remedy.

Geranium – Botanical name Pelargonium graveolens. With its sweet yet deeply floral fragrance, geranium brings balance and relaxation to a restless mind and body. It is often used in skincare to balance both dry and oily skins.

Ginger – Botanical name Zingiber officinale. Ginger has an inviting warm and spicy scent that promotes feelings of courage, comfort and contentment. Ginger oil encourages circulation, warms the blood and eases muscular discomfort.

Grapefruit – Botanical name Citrus Paradisi. Grapefruit has a bitter yet refreshing fragrance that lifts the spirits and clears the mind. Inhaling grapefruit is said to suppress appetite and ease nausea. Therapeutically, it is used to combat fluid retention and cellulite.

Jasmine – Botanical name Jasminum grandiflorum. With its intensely sweet and floral fragrance, Jasmine is one of the most comforting essential oils to treat depression and anxiety. The oil of the jasmine flower is useful during childbirth.

Juniper berry – Botanical name Juniperus communis. Juniper has a kind of sweet almost pine tree type of scent, and is believed to be highly purifying psychologically. Best known for its diuretic properties, juniper is also used treat fluid retention and arthritis.

Lavender – Botanical name Lavendula augustifolia. The pleasant floral fragrance of lavender promotes peace and relaxation. Lavender is a widely used because it has many therapeutic benefits, helping to treat burns, bites, wounds, headaches and muscle pain.

Lemon – Botanical name Citrus limon. The fresh scent of lemon oil is purifying and refreshing, promoting feelings of clarity. Lemon oil has a toning effect on the circulatory system.

Lemongrass – Botanical name Cymbopogon flexuosus. Having a strong grassy and herbaceous citrus scent makes lemongrass an energising oil that will supports awareness and concentration. Lemongrass is used to help with indigestion and other digestive disorders.

Lemon Myrtle – Botanical name Backhousia citriodora. Lemon myrtle has an intense citrus fragrance that is used to revive the senses and support overall wellbeing. It is beneficial for headaches and muscle pain.

Lime – Botanical name Citrus aurantifolia. Lime has a refreshing and zesty aroma, making it a perfect oil to promote energy and mental clarity. Lime oil is antibacterial and is good for those with oily skin.

Mandarin – Botanical name Citrus reticulate. The sweet and slightly bitter smell of mandarin oil calms feelings of stress and sadness. It is good for babies and children because it helps relieve anxiety, colic and indigestion.

May Chang – Botanical name Litsea cubeba. Emitting a strong sort of fruity like aroma, May Chang is used to alleviate stress and anxiety and is useful in helping to lower blood pressure. May Chang also helps to ease pain in the body.

Neroli – Botanical name Citrus aurantium. Neroli has a beautifully fresh and light floral perfume. It is well known for helping depression, anxiety, and insomnia.

Nutmeg – Botanical name Myristica fragrans. With its distinctly warm and spicy aroma nutmeg is used to lift the spirits and warm the body. Nutmeg is a digestive stimulant and is good for relieving muscular aches and pains.

Orange – Botanical name Citrus aurantium. Orange oil has a sweet and joyful smell that leaves you feeling relaxed and happy. Orange oil has a toning effect when used in skincare. It blends perfectly with other citrus and floral essential oils.

Palmarosa – Botanical name Cymbopogon martini. Palmarosa has a deep floral odour similar to rose oil, and also shares its ability to calm nervous anxiety and stress. Palmarosa is broadly used in skincare due to its balancing, repairing and hydrating properties.

Patchouli – Botanical name Pogostemon cablin. Patchouli has a richly aromatic and woody scent, and the earthy aroma allows one to feel grounded, calm and supported. Patchouli oil has antifungal properties and is beneficial for dry and cracked skin.

Petitgrain – Botanical name Citrus aurantium. Petitgrain has an interesting slightly floral and woody smell that is said to stimulate an intellectual mind. Petitgrain oil can be used to help with insomnia, and in skincare it is used to balance oily acne-prone skin.

Peppermint – Botanical name Mentha piperita. Peppermint an extremely refreshing fragrance that promotes mental clarity. It is also a remedy for digestive upsets and headaches. Peppermint oil has a cooling effect when applied to the body.

Pine – Botanical name Pinus silvestris. It has a distinctly fresh and spicy-sweet like aroma. It is a tonic to the lungs when inhaled, helping with a range of bronchial problems.

Rose – Botanical name Rosa centifolia. Enjoyed for its delightfully sweet and floral odour profile, rose oil is regarded as the flower oil with the highest energetic vibration. Rose oil is used to support and comfort those suffering with grief and trauma, and is also effective for calming red and dry skin.

Rosemary – Botanical name Rosmarinus officinalis. Having an herbaceous and woody like aroma, rosemary is used to support concentration and memory. Rosemary oil is highly stimulating. It encourages hair growth and circulation.

Sandalwood – Botanical name Santalum album. With its sweet, soft and woody perfume, sandalwood is a highly valued essential oil for the deep relaxation and comforting feelings it offers. In skincare, sandalwood oil brings relief to dry and irritated skin.

Spearmint – Botanical name Mentha spicata. Spearmint has a smooth, warm and herbaceous aroma. It has an uplifting effect that helps with fatigue and exhaustion. It is excellent for flatulence and digestive complaints.

Tea tree – Botanical name Melaleuca alternifolia. Having a deeply spicy and fresh odour profile, tea tree is used to strengthen immunity. It is highly recognised for its antifungal, antibacterial and antiviral properties, and is commonly used to treat an array of bacterial infections.

Vetiver – Botanical name Vetiveria zizanioides. Vetiver has a heavy woody scent and is good for those in need of support during periods of emotional stress and depression. Vetiver oil can be used to assist both physical and mental exhaustion.

Ylang Ylang – Botanical name Cananga odorata. Ylang ylang has a deeply sweet, floral and heady perfume that is powerful for easing feelings of anger and distress. It is also an aphrodisiac and has an antidepressant effect. It is balancing in skincare products, and suitable for pretty much all skin types.

"More than ever before, we need to reconnect our lives to a more holistic lifestyle. *Hippies in the City* is the perfect guide. It will change the way you think about food and wellbeing. Rita eloquently shares with us her intense passion for life and natural therapies. Written in an easy to follow and engaging format, it is full of so much practical and insightful information. This book comes from the heart."
Salvatore Battaglia,
author of The Complete Guide to Aromatherapy

"Thank you Rita - this book is such a gift. A rich menu for living, it comes from the heart and a life well-lived. Luscious recipes and accessible information make it such a fantastic resource for a vital and healthy life." Thank you for re-defining 'hippy'.
Carolyn Stubbin,
author of Do it Yourself Pure Plant Skin Care

"*Hippies In The City* is a wonderful, comprehensive guide to living a healthier, more inspired life. From healthy food, skincare, exercise, love and life, this is a little treasure to be shared by grandmothers, mothers and daughters".
Carla Oates,
author of Feeding Your Skin

"*Hippies In The City* is a wise, funny and gentle guide reminding us to stay centered and natural amid the whir of city life. I think I'll take Rita's advice and buy one for my handbag and a few extra to leave in offices, trains and planes around the world for all those fellow blossoming bohemians out there!"
Zoe Tuckwell-Smith,
actress and bonafide Hippy In The City

"Rita Balshaw's book will do a tremendous service to anyone who picks it up and reads it. It is impossible to come away from this book and not somehow feel that you've been psychologically detoxed. Apart from the well researched and scientifically informed content, the thing that gives this book a unique coherence is its attitude to food, which, readers will soon discover, represents one aspect of a whole approach to life. It's really a philosophy of food and the good life, a blending of Plato with Jamie Oliver. Everyone has a philosophy of some sort or another, and the essential difference between philosophers and non-philosophers is that philosophers know they have a philosophy. You may not agree with the philosophy that underpins the material presented in this book, but you will be grateful for the delightful arrangement of useful and easily assimilated facts and advice. Personally, I will be giving a copy of Hippies In The City to several friends and family members."
John Zerilli,
author of The Economic Imperative

"*Hippies In The City* is full of really great ideas, executed in a very contemporary way!"
Vanessa Gray,
founder of Vanessa Megan Organic Skincare Products

"*Hippies In The City* is an amazing book that inspires you to lead a healthy lifestyle, with its emphasis on ancient wisdom, organic foods and natural therapies. I appreciate Rita for this wonderful guide to achieving absolute health of body, mind and soul."
Dr Tsering Thakchoe Drungtso,
Chairman (CCTM)

"*Hippies In The City* is a must-read for anyone seeking a complete connection to their mind, body and spirit. I thoroughly agree that food has a massive affect on the way we feel. This book is intelligent, extremely helpful, warm, down-to-earth and from the heart – just like the wonderful woman who wrote it."
Faye De Lanty,
TV presenter and owner of Fashion Hound

"*Hippies In The City* is a great read. Very inspiring!"
Dr John Sugiharto,
Founder of Soma High Vibe Foods Café

"This is an awesome read. It has changed my life!"
Drew Courtney,
Pro Surfer

"*Hippies In The City* is a magical exploration of our precious connection to nature. If you're not a hippy in the city already, this book will make you want to be one."
Claudia Blaxell,
author of Spellbinding

"What a delight it was to read this book. Bright and easy and so informative, I actually caught myself smiling whilst reading. For me, the fact that Rita is a living example of what she has written makes all the difference. Well done on making a difference in this hectic and harried world we live in Miss Rita."
Janene Tomelty,
Anti-Ageing Expert

Rita Balshaw, Certified Health and Wellness Coach, savvy ambassador of natural therapies, gives her readers and fans the inspiration and confidence to transform mind, body and spirit and embrace a holistic approach to living. Rita grew up on the Central Coast of New South Wales and currently lives in Bondi, NSW.

To purchase a copy of this book visit
www.hippiesinthecity.com

 www.facebook.com/
hippiesinthecity

 @hippiesinthecity
#hippiesinthecity